4/18

Drugstore
Memories

DRUGSTORE MEMORIES
American Pharmacists Recall Life
Behind the Counter
1824 - 1933

as edited by

Glenn Sonnedecker

David L. Cowen

Gregory J. Higby

American Institute of the History of Pharmacy
Madison, Wisconsin
2002

Publication No. 20 (New Series)
Gregory J. Higby and Elaine C. Stroud, General Editors

American Institute of the History of Phramacy
University of Wisconsin School of Pharmacy
777 Highland Ave.
Madison, WI 53705
www.aihp.org

FRONT COVER: This corner drugstore, as painted in 1927 by the artist Edward Hopper, conveys a reassuring nighttime scene familiar to most Americans of the time. As in many canvases by Hopper, an urban realism is tinged with a feeling of loneliness.

Drug Store; 1927
By: Edward Hopper, American 1882-1967
Oil on canvas; 73.66 x 101.92 cm (29 x 40 1/8 in.)
Museum of Fine Arts, Boston; Bequest of John T. Spaulding; 48.564

BACK COVER: The elegant dress of this community pharmacist, photographed in 1900, contrasts with the well-worn character of his prescription room. (Photo courtesy of the American Pharmaceutical Association Foundation Archives, and George B. Griffenhagen.)

ISBN:0-931292-38-7

Contents

Dates indicate the approximate time-span of each author's observations. Chronologically arranged.

Preface

HERE are ordinary practitioners, telling in their own words what it was like behind the counter. They hail from places as far apart as a teeming, immigrant neighborhood in New York and a sparsely settled Texas cowtown. They are voices of a past long gone in pharmacy, times as far apart as the days when the Revolution still was an exciting first-hand memory, and the days when these typical small entrepreneurs were struggling against the Great Depression.

We searched out first-hand testimonies, unpolished and unexpurgated, which were scattered in reminiscences, diaries, memoirs, letters, and the like—published and unpublished. These accounts are not history in any formal sense, but offer vivid glimpses of a vanished work-a-day world out of which present-day pharmacists evolved and inherited occupational mind-sets to be nurtured or to be surmounted. An individual's recollection can of course be biased by life circumstances, or be faulty because of the memory slippage inflicted by time. Yet, this is not the place to apply the historian's rules for evaluating and interpreting the sources. Our more modest purpose is to rescue these unique sources from the risk of being lost. Some are from defunct and disintegrating journals now more than a century old. Some are from publications to which crowded pharmacy libraries are tempted to apply the fatal euphemism, "deaccession," since they now have "only" historical value. But our contrary belief that these voices from long ago are worth preserving, even if read simply for their inherent interest, motivated this small anthology.

While reader interest may seem diminished by multiple accounts of similar experiences, independent testimonies to the same concern or practice suggests greater believability. And the very act of selecting what to tell us from their years of experience makes it more likely that these practitioners are saying something characteristic or defining about the practice of pharmacy in their time. This can be a different reality, in some respects, from that we draw from the manuals, dispensatories, and the like that come down to us from a pharmacist's bookshelf.

So it has seemed worthwhile to reintroduce in these pages 59 practitioners—brought together from more than a century of American history—who collectively left behind a unique record of the pharmacy that was—that ever changing mix of trade and craft, business and profession.

A Note on Method

The 59 accounts have been searched out in a variety of sources: old journals, out-of-print books, manuscript diaries and correspondence, even one court testimony. For the most part these are unpretentious accounts of life behind the counter while learning or practicing the "art of the apothecary," not inflated posturing for a place in history. Some did not take quill or pen in hand until four or five decades after their experiences; others set down their impressions shortly after the events. A representative balance among the generations of pharmacists scarcely could be expected; and we must be grateful for whatever came to light. The period 1860-1920 was especially productive, probably in part because it was a period of memorable change in pharmacy, technologically and professionally. About eighty documents that we identified as potentially useful proved to be inappropriate for the present purpose or were not available to us. To be eligible for consideration, an account had to be first-hand observations by an author now deceased, who had practiced pharmacy (retail and/or wholesale) in the USA at some time. Given these criteria, the accounts located and available have limited the period represented to about 1824 to 1933.

From these original accounts we present only selected passages that relate to pharmacy. Since *the main text thus consists entirely of direct quotations,* we omit a myriad of quotation marks that otherwise would be required (except where they appeared in the original account). Words occasionally added by the Editors, to explain or clarify, are designated by square brackets. We frequently took the liberty of not bracketing minor alterations that clarify without changing meaning, such as adding a punctuation mark, spelling out an obscure abbreviation, or adding a preposition or an article. Omission of material repetitious or irrelevant, whatever the length, is indicated by ellipsis marks (. . .). Because reminiscences can be disorganized or rambling, in a few instances we violated a scholarly stricture by moving a passage to a spot adjacent to other information on the same subject. A complete citation of the source of each excerpt is given in the Bibliography. At the beginning of each excerpt in the main text, the reader will note the practitioner's name, birth and death dates if known, and the place and time-period in which the experiences occurred.

Acknowledgments

The editors acknowledge with warm appreciation the repositories and publishers that have helped to preserve the recollections here excerpted. Passages drawn from copyrighted books are specifically credited to the following publishers at the end of such excerpts: McGraw Hill Book Company (*Drugstore Days* . . .); American Pharmaceutical Association (*The Remington Lectures*); Meyer Brothers (*The Earlier Years* . . .); Wm. L. Blockstein and C. Boyd Granberg (*Remarkable Pharmacists*); University of Pennsylvania Press (*A Quaker Forty-Niner* . . .); F. A. Davis Co. (*Muskets and Medicine* . . .); and Prentice-Hall, Inc. (*The Casual Biography of a Prairie Town*). We are likewise grateful to the University of Wisconsin School of Pharmacy, especially to Nancy Randall, and to the American Institute of the History of Pharmacy, especially to Elaine Condouris Stroud, Ph.D., for major help in bringing this small volume to press. The historical illustrations are drawn from the F. B. Power Pharmaceutical Library and Edward Kremers Reference Files of the University of Wisconsin-Madison, with the exception of the front cover (Museum of Fine Arts, Boston), back cover (American Pharmaceutical Association Foundation Archives), and pages 21 (Rutgers University Library), 40 (Smithsonian Institution), 113, 115, 116 (Denver Public Library). The original source of an illustration is acknowledged at the end of its caption, if known.

Part I:
1824-1860

INTRODUCTION

As THE APOTHECARIES, pharmacists, and physicians unfold their stories in the following pages, it becomes vividly evident that the history of pharmacy in the United States reflects in detail the history of the country. Pharmacy did not develop *in vacuo.* The sparse population in colonial times—a population spread over thirteen separate political jurisdictions—and the existence of but a handful of cities, was not conducive to attracting trained apothecaries to our shores. Although the need for men "skillful in all kinds of drugs" was noted by explorers of the New World as early as 1584, few came to British North America as practitioners of pharmacy. Perhaps the first trained apothecary who came to practice his profession and actually did so was Robert Cooke who arrived in Boston in 1638, but there were few like him in British and Dutch North America for many years to follow.

In the colonial period, and indeed throughout the antebellum period in the nineteenth century, the practice of pharmacy was in the hands of a variety of functionaries—the physician who, in addition to his diagnosing, compounded (or had his apprentice compound) and directly dispensed his medicines; the apothecary who, like his British counterpart, also diagnosed, prescribed, compounded and dispensed medicines; the druggist, who though a

1

wholesaler nevertheless also ran a retail pharmacy; the pharmacist, who ran a retail establishment concerned largely with compounding and dispensing drugs (increasingly upon a doctor's prescription) and with the sale of related and often unrelated items; and the general merchant who carried a line of medicines and sometimes evolved into a pharmacist. The appellations druggist and pharmacist were to be synonyms and lost any distinction.

This arrangement was becoming outmoded by 1860, under a variety of influences. A growing number of physicians prospered without also practicing as pharmacists, especially in heavily settled areas. Among physicians who abjured shop-keeping, many continued to dispense drugs from their medical offices and on their rounds through the countryside, but depended on independent druggists to maintain their drug stock. In urban centers, where highly skilled pharmacists were becoming common, an increasing number of physicians adopted the practice of writing prescriptions for a patient—perhaps welcoming the opportunity to give up what they tended to view as the inferior craft of the practice of pharmacy. But financial necessity frequently dictated the mode of practice.

The expansion of the country westward and the absence of regulatory requirements made the entrance into the practice of pharmacy a matter mainly of personal choice and enterprise. That is not to say that there were not spotty attempts to require the examination and licensing of pharmacists. In Louisiana such requirements went back to its time as a French colony and no fewer than 130 "registered" pharmacists can be counted by 1847. Even in Louisiana, however, all statutory requirements for regulating pharmacy (and medicine and dentistry) were repealed in 1852, bringing Louisiana into the mainstream of the American *laissez-faire* milieu. Three other states of the South, possibly following the Louisiana lead, attempted to regulate pharmacy. Although there are records of twenty-one licensed pharmacists in South Carolina and of five in Georgia before the Civil War (with only presumptive evidence of licensure in Alabama), the regulations "became dead letters upon the statute books." The *ad hominem* spirit of Jacksonian Democracy is illustrated by the pronouncement of a Mr. Day, a physician, to the Louisiana legislature in the debate over the repeal of regulatory legislation in 1852: After mentioning "a wild agrarian notion of our natural rights," Day went on to declaim, "If, Mr.

Speaker, men desired to dose themselves with medicine, at the hands of ignorant and unskilled persons, let them have that privilege."

Practitioners who had any training in pharmacy received that training, as *Drugstore Memories* so amply illustrates, through apprenticeship. The length of term varied, but the rigor of the indenture is obvious. The quality of the training depended upon the knowledge, abilities, and sense of responsibility of the preceptor. However, in 1821, the Philadelphia College of Pharmacy opened and began the education of the pharmacists theoretically as well as practically. By the Civil War four other such colleges were established, the Massachusetts College of Pharmacy in Boston, the College of Pharmacy of the City of New York, the Maryland College of Pharmacy in Baltimore, and the Chicago College of Pharmacy. The educational offerings of these local societies varied; they offered regular programs or, as in the case of the Boston school, only occasional lectures. Thus, although only occasional references to the colleges do turn up in these *Memories*, their importance is indicated by the fact that the Philadelphia College of Pharmacy listed just over 400 graduates between 1826 and 1860. In fact, by 1860 there was a total of 514 graduates throughout the country, out of a total of 11,000 pharmacists. The training received in the colleges was in addition to, and not a replacement for, apprenticeship or other practical experience in a pharmacy.

The "bible" of the pharmacist in the antebellum period, to quote one of the *Memories*, was the *Dispensatory of the United States*, the first edition of which appeared in 1833. It and the *United States Pharmacopoeia*, the first edition of which appeared in 1820, were both the work of physicians, an indication of the involvement of physicians in early American pharmacy. *Drugstore Memories* also reveals that along with these two authorities, chemistry texts were important to the practicing pharmacist. Not until 1849 did the American pharmacist have an American textbook as a guide. In that year William Procter put out an American edition of Theophilus Redwood's translation of Carl Friedrich Mohr's German work, under the title *Practical Pharmacy: The Arrangements, Apparatus, and Manipulations of the Pharmaceutical Shop and Laboratory*. In 1856 another Philadelphia pharmacist, Edward Parrish, issued his *Introduction to Practical Pharmacy*, intended for both physician and pharmacist. The pharmacist also had a professional journal after the Philadelphia College of Pharmacy began to issue in 1825 what was later called the *American Journal of Pharmacy*.

Drugstore Memories includes little mention of botany, especially surprising since Thomsonian medicine, with its botanical basis, flourished during the antebellum period. The drugstore of the time—and for a long time to come—carried a full line of simples (mainly crude botanical drugs) and chemicals with which the pharmacist compounded and dispensed medicines with or without a prescription. Smith, Moore & Co. of New York, had advertised itself in 1784 as "A store, mixt, various, universal," justifiably so, for its inventory came from all corners of the earth and covered the whole range of the materia pharmaceutica.

The antebellum pharmacist practiced *secundum artem*. He was an artisan who spread his own plasters and prepared pills, powders, tinctures, ointments, syrups, conserves, medicated waters, and perfumes. Economic necessity forced him to handle such commodities as confections, tobacco, paints and glass, groceries, spices, and liquor. He was thus commonly also a merchant; and pharmacists themselves—as evident in our collected testimonies—often differed as to whether theirs was a trade or a profession. Elias Durand, a Philadelphia pharmacist, installed in his shop about 1825 what was certainly one of the first soda fountains in the country. The soda fountain was to become a distinguishing feature of the drugstore for well into the twentieth century.

Slight inroads on the artisanal role of the pharmacist were evident by mid-nineteenth century. For example, in 1849 Hall, Merrick, and Haskell of New York introduced a series of powders "put up in 1 pound bottles in green paper that were hailed as a boon by [the pharmaceutist]." *Drugstore Memories* makes it clear that the wholesale drug dealer was often also a manufacturer, and the pharmacist had to rely on the chemical industry to provide him with the new alkaloids that were coming out of Europe. The burgeoning growth of proprietary ("patent") medicines, flamboyantly advertised, forced the pharmacist to deal with them. Economic competition from department stores, groceries, and chain stores added to the pressure.

All of this can be gleaned from these *Memories*. Yet, one thing is missing in these memories of the early years: the characteristic fragrance of the American drugstore. Although the odors of drugs are cited, it is almost as if the writers took the fragrance of the drugstore for granted. But the visitor guided into a shop blindfolded would recognize immediately that he was in a drugstore, a store "mixt, various and universal."

Note: The recollections excerpted in this booklet are wholly quotations from the original sources cited in the Bibliography.—The Editors

REMINISCENCES

William A. Brewer, Sr. (b. 1807-d. 1890)
Boston, Massachusetts, c.1824-1860s

In Boston sixty years ago [the 1820s] the several stores which were designated as wholesale drug establishments [all] combined the retail and dispensing prescription business. But each department was conducted separately, the front part of the lower floor being devoted to retail and prescription business, and the rear to the counting-room and the packing of goods for city and country stores. Such was the establishment where the deponent was ensconced as an apprentice.

Our store was four stories high, with an ample attic—the building being twenty-five feet wide and one hundred and twelve feet deep, and extending from Washington (then Cornhill) Street to Devonshire Street in the rear, where we received and discharged heavy packages. The second story was divided into several rooms, each having its distinct use; e.g., the front room was the sleeping room of two of the older clerks, who answered the night-bell; the next room was used for packages or bundles of dry articles, such as roots of various kinds, and junk-bottles of tinctures and other fluids, all marked with their several weights and labelled, and ready for the packer. So when orders came in, no time was lost in weighing out the several articles. No idleness was allowed, and on rainy days, or when orders flagged, the clerks were employed in putting up these bundles and bottles, and placing them in their appropriate apartments on the shelves. There were 1-lb., 2-lb., 3-lb., and 4-lb. bundles of valerian, pink root, and other roots, and bottles of about 1-1/2 lbs. containing, e.g., Tinctura Rhei, Tinctura Lavendulae Composita, as also Spiritus Nitri Dulcis, Tinctura Myrrhae et Aloes (then often called Elixir Proprietatis, or Elixir Pro for short), and Tinctura Sennae Composita (then called Elixir Salutis), and others—castor oil bringing up the rear.

7

The next room on our second floor was devoted principally to flint-glass wares made at the glasshouses at South Boston and East Cambridge, Mass., including vials and bottles of every required capacity, retorts, receivers, separating funnels, Wolfe's bottles, eudiometers, tubes of various calibre, etc., etc. One side of this room, however, was occupied with imported chemical, philosophical, and pharmaceutical wares—glass, earthen, and iron retorts; Wedgwood's evaporating dishes, mortars and pestles, pill tiles, etc.; electrical cylinders of all sizes; graduated measures of every usual capacity; etc., etc.

The room beyond, upon the same floor, was adapted to a lecture room for several courses of lectures by physicians. . . . At intervals the same room was occupied as a dissecting-room for young medical students. The writer had the privilege of attending all the above lectures and of witnessing all the dissections. The "subjects" were obtained from the burial-ground for paupers on "Boston Neck". . . . The writer acted as watchman at the back door of our store, and on hearing bells approaching at midnight, received the stiffly frozen corpses from the sleigh, where each had been placed bolt-upright between two young Aesculapiuses. . . . But all this was an episode not necessarily connected with the business of a druggist or pharmacist, to which I had devoted myself.

Our third floor was divided into two apartments, the one containing powdered drugs in barrels and boxes, all distinctly labelled. Most of these powders that were required in large quantities were ground and bolted at the mills in the suburbs of Boston. But perhaps the greater number, comprising articles required in smaller quantities, were powdered in the store, in the basement. There a heavy post was set in the ground, surmounted with a large bell-metal mortar, with a wrought-iron pestle of great weight. And here I would remark, our several mortars for use in the establishment, of different sizes, as well as all our sets of weights from half an ounce to fifty-six pounds, were of bell-metal, and were imported from England. All our copper counter-scales, large and small, were also imported from England, such things being practically unobtainable of good quality in this country at the early date of my inauguration in pharmacy. . . .

The rear room on this same (third) floor was occupied for the manufacture of tinctures, syrups, etc., and each apprentice had to spend six months in their manufacture under the tutelage of one of the older clerks. The process was by steeping or digesting the solids for tinctures in the prescribed menstruum, decanting, filtering, etc. The system of percolation was adopted in after years, and the theory that each portion of the menstruum carries down its full portion of soluble matter from the solid ingredients was fully established. The tyro had no established *vade mecum* for his guidance, as we have now in the U. S. Pharmacopoeia; for the Edinburgh Dispensatory and Thacher's American Dispensatory and private receipt-books were used according to the fancy or prejudices of the principals of the various drug-stores. There was more or less a want of uniformity in the preparations issued from different establishments. . . . Even when in 1820 the first edition of the U. S. Pharmacopoeia appeared, it did not command the confidence of the best pharmacists, nor the universal respect of the medical faculty, even after it was buttressed by "Bigelow's Sequel," which in turn admitted of some revamping to make it consistent. It is a curious fact that some city physicians, and more rural ones—from whose ranks we had many customers who carried their medicines in their saddle-bags—rejected the preparations made according to these new books, preferring such as we made according to our private recipes. . . .

Like many "druggists" of the nineteenth century, Thomas Dyott of Philadelphia (above) supplied both wholesale and retail service. Druggist William Brewer recalls here what it was like inside the similar establishment where he worked in Boston. (Engraving from T. Porter, The Picture of Philadelphia, *1831.)*

In one corner of this room was a quaint mill standing upon four legs, containing an "upper and nether mill-stone," for grinding cream of tartar—all sold by us being ground under our own roof. Our sales were not so extensive as in most wholesale stores of the present day. Our porter ground about 125 lbs. per day when working uninterrupt-edly. When called off to other duties, the boys would turn the crank in his place. There was also in another corner a mercury mill for reducing the globules of quicksilver prior to the manufacture of Unguentum Hydrargyri. This consisted of a two-gallon bell-metal mortar set in a lignum-vitae frame, a pestle or muller of iron, with an X face moved around by cog-wheels and a hand crank. It was the business of one of the older clerks to weigh out the mercury and the suet or lard for the porter, whose duty it was to do the levigation. Some of the old books directed a small quantity of balsam of sulphur to be put in. . . .

[*From Pt. 3*: For large-scale drug milling there was] on Wheeler's Point a grist-mill where cream of tartar and other bulky drugs were ground. [One customer], the drug firm of Rice, Henshaw and Co. of Boston, probably the largest house in that trade in the United States, sent five casks—each about 1000 to 1200 lbs.—cream of tartar to be powdered at the mill on Wheeler's Point. When the powder was re-turned, the specific gravity, or some incidental attraction, led Mr. Henshaw to have the product analyzed. The result showed an admix-ture of twenty per centum of Potassae et Aluminae Sulphas, or com-mon refined alum, enabling the miller to keep one entire cask of the tartar [that had been supplied]. . . . The cupidity of the miller was re-warded by a term of five years in the State prison. . . .

[*From Pt. 4:*] Now, return to the third floor of the old store where the writer received his tutelage as a druggist and pharmacist. . . . In the hallway between the powder-room and the mill-room—as we were accustomed to designate them—there was a broad stair case lead-ing to the fourth loft, and the remaining space was occupied by a pile of ceroons of Peruvian bark. . . .

When the writer enlisted as a novice in the store of Bartlett & Brewer, there remained about sixty ceroons of the original purchase. On opening the ceroons, each was found to contain a certificate either in Spanish or Portuguese from the government of the state or province where the bark was collected, certifying that it was the true yellow or Calisaya cinchona bark. . . .

In those days my employers supplied Harvard, Brown, and other universities with chemicals and chemical and philosophical apparatus and utensils for their laboratories and lecture-tables, from abroad to a considerable extent. Platina wire and crucibles, agate and steel mortars for crushing gems, Pappin's digesters for preparing bones for articulated skeletons, and Davy's safety lamps for illustrating to students its principles in ether and inflammable gases, probably were introduced in this country, at the demand of these institutions, by my employers.

[*From Pt. 5:*] Now trudge up to the prosaic fourth story of my youthful habitation. . . . This story was also divided into two apartments—the rear one being exclusively devoted to the storage of glass ware in packages. The front apartment was used for the storage of bulky commodities, such as licorice root, orange peel, gentian root, pink root, etc. And here I would say, in passing, Spigelia marilandica in those days came to us exclusively with the tops on, which feature was quite objectionable as the leaves and stalks were of little or no medicinal value; and moreover intertwined with the stalks was a vine of irritant if not poisonous character. The separation of the roots, as at the present day [1885], is every way an economic custom.

Orange peel and gentian in bales occupied the larger part of this loft, being piled up from floor to ceiling; for these were perhaps more in demand in those days when almost everybody indulged in Stoughton's elixir as morning bitters. . . .

The more interesting part of the store where I had my early training was the retail department, or pharmacy proper. Here, after the store was opened at a very early hour, with my green baize apron adjusted, fires were made in cold weather, lamps were trimmed, floor swept and sanded, counters and show-cases dusted. These preliminaries for business having been discharged, the novice was duly instructed by older clerks in making and tying small square bundles. There were drawers for cream of tartar and sulphur, epsom salts, senna, and manna, etc.—popular articles of every-day sale—in one-ounce packages. Then followed instructions as to the characters upon the apothecaries' weights from one grain to two drachms; Troyweights from a pennyweight to one pound; and avoirdupois weights from one eighth of an ounce to fifty-six pounds; and critical instructions and examinations in the use of graduated glass measures.

After these lessons, followed an examination of all the solid substances in the drawers, with the Dispensatory in hand, so that a knowledge of the sources of production, general appearance, qualities, and uses might be acquired. . . .

Mr. Chase, the predecessor of my older brother as junior partner, was a man of consummate taste. When he came into the concern where the writer was afterwards matriculated, he rejuvenated the retail department throughout. The prescription desk was considered—if not a model—superior to anything in Boston. It was of mahogany, about six feet in length, two feet in depth from front to rear, and eighteen inches high in the back.

Upon the rear part of the table or counter were several shallow drawers containing: letter paper cut into squares of different sizes (with gilded edges) for powders; small earthen and porcelain jars and boxes for eye and other ointments; and pink and white paper pill-boxes (the first paper pill-boxes introduced into this country, from the manufactory of Messrs. John Robinson & Son, Wheatbridge, near Sheffield, England). Above these shallow drawers were two shelves with socketed racks, in which stood rows of glass-stoppered bottles containing all the more commonly required powders for answering prescriptions, and a few bottles containing pills of proper size for ordinary use, such as opium, hydrarg., saponis, etc. On the table rested the prescription scales of two sizes upon a mahogany base, with silver pans and chains. Under the table was a long shallow drawer containing all sizes of iron ointment spatulas; steel pallet-knives; marble, glass, and Wedgwood's mortars and pestles; marble, Wedgwood's, and earthen pill-tiles; brass pill-machines, etc. Silver and pearl spatulas for pills and powders lay upon a damask napkin in front of the prescription scales. . . . Beneath the table or dispensing counter there were drawers for the various sizes of chip ointment boxes, plaster skins, plaster irons, etc., besides tin-lined drawers containing the ordinary pill masses, such as asafoetida, saponis, rufi, cocciae, plumeri, etc.

[*From Pt. 8:*] The old laboratory, or "still-house" . . . was a large apartment with plain brick walls on all sides. In the brick floor there was an iron grating about two feet square where the slightly descending floor from the four corners converged to carry all washings into the sewer.

On one side were three brick furnaces, one for calcining magnesia, one for distilling Aqua Ammoniae, and a third for a large sand-bath for glass retorts and evaporating dishes. On another side was a large, open fire-place, with a crane and trammels for the suspension of kettles for plasters, etc. On the same side was a copper-still of one hundred gallons capacity, set in a brick furnace, and furnished with a copper head, and a coiled tin worm immersed in an iron-bound upright tub of oft-refrigerated water.

Small moveable sand and water baths stood round here and there, as silent witnesses to the more important operations in the large

furnaces, yet ready to serve the operators in any humble capacity during more delicate manipulations in chemistry.

On a third side of the room stood a heavy oaken press, fastened to the wall with iron clamps and bolts, which was used in pressing out "Stoughton's Bitters," of which we usually prepared a hogshead full at one time. Some other tinctures in less quantity were pressed in this press previous to the introduction of the portable iron tincture presses. Another use of this large press was in pressing herbs of all sorts into half-pound cakes. Each cake was separated from its fellows by wrought-iron plates of exact dimensions to fit the strong box into which the herbs were crowded after having been carefully trimmed of stems and picked free from dead or discolored leaves. Our porters, not being allowed to be in idleness during business hours, were required to fill momentary lulls in heavier work by keeping the press-box filled with herbs. When the full number of cakes that the box would contain had been put under the strongest pressure which one or two men with a heavy crow-bar could bring to bear upon them, they were left for a few hours before being taken out and put into papers of two cakes of one pound each, then labelled by the clerks. We bought rather more than half our pressed herbs from the Shakers; the balance required for our sales were brought to us by country people whom we contracted with year by year. As the place of the writer's summering in vacation-times abounded with stramonium and the different species of savin, he used to gather a small wagon-load from time to time and take the herbs into Boston, where it was a pride and delight to make them up into ointments and cerates "green as a leek". . . .

On the fourth side of the laboratory were tables for rolling plasters, which were moulded into one-half pound and pound rolls, enveloped in white or blue paper, crimped with the thumbnail on the ends, and labelled ready for sale. The different plasters were made in quantities to suit the demand, and consisted principally of emp. diach. (lead plaster)—of which we usually made one hundred pounds at a time—emp. diach. c.g., emp. stom. oliveri, emp. catharid., emp. oxid. ferri, emp. hydrarg., emp. flor. unguenti, emp. melilot., emp. oxycroc., emp. adhesiv., emp. hydrarg. c. ammon., emp. roborans, emp. cumini, emp. c. minio, emp. anodynym, and emp. saponis. We tyros, superintended by an older clerk as boss pro tem, were required to weigh out and get together the various ingredients required for any particular plaster, and with the Dispensatory in hand—the pharmacist's Bible in those days—to proceed *secundum artem* to finish up our alloted job. . . .

In early times all the alcohol used and sold by the firm . . . was distilled in our laboratory. Three barrels of New England rum were put into the still together with some fifteen to twenty pounds of heated and dry pearl-ash, and a fire kindled. From this the product was one barrel of 95 alcohol, and one barrel of low-wines to be used as rum in the next distillation. For anhydrous alcohol, 95 alcohol was re-distilled in glass retorts placed in sand-baths, and condensed in glass receivers immersed in ice. . . .

[*From Pt. 16:*] About a decade after embarking in business on my own account [c. 1837], the onerous system of sending out traveling salesmen was introduced from abroad. Travellers from England and France had periodically visited us to increase sales, . . . but no jobbing-house thought of such a thing as sending out drummers through our domestic cities and towns. Merchants had their warehouses and their stocks of goods, and waited for those who desired to make purchases to come where the goods were to be had. Occasionally a member of some large drug-house in New York, Philadelphia, or Baltimore called upon us. . . .

Ultimately the system of sending out employes to "scare up trade" became so much the fashion that any one who did not fall in with the mode would have been regarded as a fossil trilobite or some other paleontological specimen, and left behind in the race. But sometimes the system seems slavishly abnormal and expensive, and in some of its aspects is horribly oppressive if not decidedly immoral—not in the drug trade alone, but in many other lines of business. For example, many a young man has been sent out on a drumming tour with expensive trunks of samples and a pocketful of cash, with *carte-blanche* to spend whatever may be deemed expedient to induce retailers and others to buy their goods. These young men put up at the best hotels oftentimes and entertain buyers at their rooms, where they display their samples, smoking lavishly the choicest cigars and drinking the best wines and liquors. Perchance at the end of their chaffering, the parties would emerge to enjoy the luxuries of a concert-room, theatre, or brothel—all at the expense of the principal who sends forth the drummer.

J. Brown Baxley (b. 1814- d. 1896), Baltimore, Maryland, and Mobile, Alabama, 1830-1850

As an older brother had served an army post (fort) where Chicago now stands, for a long time without any substantial worldly possessions, father vigorously opposed another son following that example. Consequently, through the mediation of another older brother, Dr. Henry Willis Baxley, . . . the drug business, was selected for me, much against my will. Dr. Baxley applied successfully in my behalf to Messrs. Tyson and Fisher . . . who, in spite of recent establishment, en-

An American pharmacist's workplace in the 1830s, one of the earliest depictions. English influence can be seen in the shop's arrangement and shelfware. Ongoing work at the counter balance, the contusion mortar, and the filtration carboy illustrate central features of practice that endured until the early twentieth century. (From Edward Hazen, Popular Technology; or Professions and Trades, *1841 ed., Vol. I., 236.)*

joyed marked confidence of physicians and people. Mr. Fisher being a graduate of the Philadelphia College of Pharmacy gave him not a little professional distinction and prestige. But as the position required four years of apprentice service without the slightest remuneration—the custom in Baltimore—father would not listen to its acceptance, whereupon Mr. Fisher advised my going to Philadelphia. There he had been trained in the store of his uncle Samuel Powell Griffith, who then needed a clerk and would contribute board, as was the practice there—a suggestion that met hearty approval. Thus, at sixteen, 1830, I began my pharmaceutical career in that city and after remaining four years and attending, without graduation, two courses of lectures at the Philadelphia College of Pharmacy, returned to Baltimore. . . .

Shortly after, . . . I entered into the drug business with Mr. Bennett, who lived only a year, when I disposed of the store and went to Mobile, Alabama, where, forming the drug firm of Baxley and Tilghman, . . . I remained eleven years.

I experienced my first epidemic of yellow fever, having it myself, in 1837. During convalescence I met my first financial loss—the destruction of our place of business in a conflagration that included half of the city. Being unable to reestablish ourselves I took a clerkship until 1844 when, owing to the illness of my father, I returned to Baltimore. There a mere mention of having come from the distressed, fevered South, coupled with the surmise of conveying the deadly contagion (being a germ carrier), made people scan me with great apprehension and fear. That actuated largely against my securing immediate employment. Some months later I was sought as a temporary apothecary at the Baltimore General Dispensary, a position soon made permanent. I continued to hold it uninterruptedly for ten years, when I was compelled to assume management of my own retail drug store, already established in 1852 and hitherto in control of a most reliable clerk, J. Jacob Smith, who now found it to his interest to enter business elsewhere on his own account.

Robert Shoemaker (b. 1817-d. 1897), Philadelphia, 1832-1850

It was in the year 1831 that I entered one of the best known apothecary "shops" (so-called at that day) in this city, as an apprentice. . . . The store was large, situated on the corner of two of our principal streets, having three large "bulk" windows—with a show-bottle for each pane of glass, making 24 bottles to each window.

The morning work began with taking down the shutters from these windows and from two double doors, making the fire (if in cold weather), sweeping the store, cleaning and filling with sperm oil (no gas in those days) a number of lamps, which were suspended from the ceiling. The shop was opened at 6 o'clock A. M. the year round, and this daily routine of work was to be finished before breakfast.

After breakfast (the work having been laid out the day before) began the preparation of medicines—such as powdering (for, with a single exception, every powder was prepared by ourselves), the preparation of tinctures, pills, ointments, etc. *Gum* nipples were unknown—so heifer's teats trimmed out (and preserved in alcohol until wanted) and tied over the mouth of an 8 ounce bottle constituted the nursing bottle of the time. These were prepared in quantities for our own sale and for other apothecaries. I remember the bottle containing them standing right by the side of another containing clyster pipes— these to be attached to a bladder when required for use. . . .

I have said there was *one* drug we did not powder—not because it was difficult of reduction—but because my good preceptor saw fit to patronize a worthy old character named John Price, who, in a frame shanty on Callowhill street, had what he called a drug mill. In this building old friend Price had erected some rude machinery, which was set in motion by a mule. The sole attendant, the proprietor, received such easily powdered drugs as were confided to his care through an 8 by 10 aperture from an outside vestibule. None were allowed a nearer approach than this to the wonderfully constructed powdering apparatus within. Of our rhubarb [roots and rhizomes] Price would have returned, *in due time*, about two-thirds in powder—the remaining one-third in a separate package labelled "crumbs."

All else was powdered in [our] well remembered old iron mortar, so firmly seated on a stout post descending through the cellar to the earth. Ipecac, gamboge, sanguinaria and cantharides (this last moistened with alcohol) arise to my mind (and *nostrils* too) as among the particularly obnoxious articles I was obliged to reduce to a *fine* powder. Those old boxed, silk sieves were provokingly fine. . . .

A large marble mortar, of 2 or 3 gallons capacity, was stationed in one corner, firmly fixed in the open top of a keg, with a pestle of wood having a long handle, passing through a support at the top. In said mortar were always the ingredients for either mercurial ointment or blue mass [for pills]—and that old seat by the side of that mortar was never empty, except when more important duties claimed our attention. What does the modern student in pharmacy know about the luxury of *killing* mercury? Talk of a cat having 40 lives, why 40 *times* 40 will not suffice for the extinguishment of mercury; rub! rub!! rub!!! day after day, and yet the labor continues. Thankful may the modern apprentice be that this work is now [1880] done by machinery.

You will ask, "What time for study?" I will tell you: After lamp lighting, between the calls of customers, we had the privilege of reading "[John Redman] Coxe's Dispensatory," "[Edward] Turner's Chem-

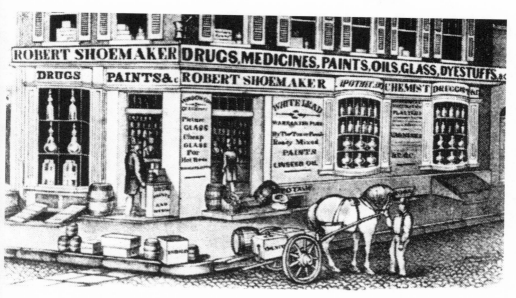

The retail and wholesale drugstore of Robert Shoemaker in Philadelphia, which he operated from 1837 to 1856. The kegs, bags, and boxes of crude drugs and finished products come and go at the entrance, via horse-drawn drays. In small-scale manufacture, Shoemaker developed a successful alternative to handmade plasters, and he may have been the first in the United States to manufacture glycerin. In this same shop Shoemaker served his apprenticeship during the 1830s, as vividly recounted in his memoir (p. 17). (Engraving from a broadside reproduced in the American Journal of Pharmacy, *104(1932): 491.)*

istry," "[Andrew] Ure's Chemical Dictionary," and, once in a quarter, the welcome "[American] Journal of Pharmacy." It is not to be wondered that, after the labors of the day, one found it difficult to keep awake throughout the long winter evenings. And I well remember how I sat, with book in one hand and a pound weight in the other, that the dropping to the floor of the weight (in case of my being overcome with drowsiness) might arouse me. . . .

In the summer of 1832 we had the first and most awful visitation of Asiatic cholera Philadelphia has ever experienced. Then it was that apothecaries had as much as they could well do, night and day. Many readers remember the camphor bags and Burgundy pitch plaster; the first worn in the bosom, suspended by a string around the neck, and the latter over the abdomen.

We had no sugar-coated pills, or fluid extracts; neither had we machine-spread plasters. Apprentices then did have some advantages over those of the present time, [for example,] their opportunities for learning the art of manufacturing were greater. The [large-scale] "manufacturing pharmaceutist" was unknown. Apothecaries (wholesale dealers alone were called "druggists") made their own preparations, and all plasters were spread by hand, as wanted (adhesive plaster, on cloth, excepted).

The experience of 1832 made many perfect in the spreading of plasters. Ten by twelve and ten by fourteen inches were not unusual sizes. Well do I remember one nervous old gentleman who, to ward off an attack of the dreaded disease, in addition to his camphor pouch, ordered a whole lambskin to be spread with Burgundy pitch, sprinkled with powdered camphor. The order was executed, the large plaster carried to his house by the writer and duly applied, covering well the stomach and abdomen. The next morning a messenger came to say that Mr. W. could not arise from his bed and dress, as the plaster had slipped down, and he required help. The removal of that plaster was a more difficult task than had been its preparation. . . . The old gentleman escaped an attack of cholera, and lived many years to proclaim the virtues of camphor and Burgundy pitch as a preventive of Asiatic cholera.

My experience in the preparation of plasters . . . led me to contrive a plan . . . to produce plasters superior to any spread by hand. From 1838 to 1850 . . . in some weeks we spread as many as 5,000 plasters. But now, with improved machinery, the preparation of plasters, porous and others, has become an important industry.

Charles E. Pancoast (b. 1818-d. 1906), Philadelphia, Pennsylvania, St. Louis and Warsaw, Missouri, 1832-1849

In October, 1832 . . . Father . . . accompanied me to Philadelphia to place me in my new position. . . . I was introduced to my new Master, John R. Rowand, and apprenticed to him to learn the Profession of an Apothecary. I was to remain with him until I reached the age of twenty-one years, he agreeing to furnish me with Board, Washing, and Clothing, and to send me for two terms to the Philadelphia

College of Pharmacy at his expense, but I was to have no spending money, for Father [a Quaker] believed spending money to be the primary cause that led Boys into evil habits. . . .

I was suddenly obliged to adopt new habits, one of the most difficult of which was to sit up and study until eleven o'clock in the evening. . . . However, I soon became initiated into the rudiments of my business, which consisted in washing Bottles, making Putty, grinding Gum Gamboge, and astringent, aromatic, or caustic Drugs that so irritated my Mouth, Nose, and Eyes that I would suffer for days from the effects of them; and wheeling the Barrow, which was the usual

A recurrent feature in Drugstore Memories *is the involvement of physicians in the practice of pharmacy. Especially during the early nineteenth century, but continuing even into the twentieth, physicians owned and operated drugstores and "doctor's shops" and entered into partnership or an employer-employee relationship with pharmacists. Illustrative of this relationship is this formal announcement by John Hardenbergh that he had bought out his former physician-partner. (Courtesy of Special Collections, Rutgers University Library.)*

New-Brunswick, October, 20, 1843.

SIR :—

Having purchased the stock and interest of my former partner, Dr. John H. Van Deursen, I shall continue the **DRUG BUSINESS** at the old stand, No. 29 Church-street, where you will always find a complete assortment of

Drugs, Medicines, Perfumery, Fancy Goods, Shakers Herbs, Patent Medicines, Leeches, Trusses, &c.

Also, PAINTS, OILS, VARNISHES, DYE STUFFS, WINDOW GLASS, and PUTTY.

Particular care and attention will be given to the preparation of Physician's prescriptions and dispensing Family medicines.

With every facility for the transaction of business, all orders will be filled with punctuality and despatch. All articles delivered will be of the choicest quality, and sold as low as they can be bought in the city.

A share of your patronage is respectfully solicited by

Your Obt. Servant,

JOHN P. HARDENBERGH.

mode of conveyance for Goods when they could not be delivered by hand. . . .

After I had been in the business about six months, Mr. Rowand opened his Heart and fitted me out with a new Suit of Clothes, so that I was enabled to dispense with the offensive little Quaker coat that had so often mortified my pride. . . .

Having now finished my education in the Rudiments, I aspired to become better informed with regard to the Art and Science of the Business, and in response to my desire my Preceptor sent me two terms to the College of Pharmacy. . . .

Before Rowand and McHenry [Rowand's new partner] closed their store—I had been with Rowand near six years—the celebrated Dr. X came into the Store and inquired for me. . . . He wanted me to engage with him at $90.00 per year and Board and Washing. I accepted his offer. . . .

Dr. X [manufactured and sold] Allibert's Hair Tonic. . . . As he had a partially bald Head, he always shrank from selling his Hair Tonic, and was disposed to turn over such customers to me, as they would impertinently ask why he did not use it on his own Head. After he had sold it about a year and finding large quantities being sold . . . he was disposed to . . . dispense with the name "Allibert" and [stop] paying Royalty [he had been paying on it]. He desired to know what I thought of the project, and I answered him I did not think it was an honorable thing to do. He was offended by my answer and spoke unkindly to me. . . .

[When the newspaper publisher] Mr. Atkinson came to the Doctor and requested an extension of the time of payment [on a loan, the Doctor] wrote out an Article extolling the virtues of his Cough Cure, which . . . he requested him to father and place in his Editorial Columns . . . The Old Gentleman appeared exceedingly embarrassed. . . . but the doctor was unrelenting . . . and so much faith had the People of Philadelphia in the word of Mr. Atkinson that we sold at Retail the following week 1000 bottles of the Cough Cure at $1.00 per bottle.

[In St. Louis, where I opened a drugstore with a partner in 1849] a young clerk who had not been in my employ six months, . . . receiving what he conceived to be a mortal insult from a Drug Clerk in another Store, . . . challenged his Insulter to meet him in Mortal

Combat on the Island. . . . The Seconds, one of whom was also a Druggist, . . . met and consulted and . . . agreed that the Druggist Second should make up some fresh Bolus of the Size of the Pistol bore and load the Pistols with them. . . . On the day appointed, the Combatants . . . were punctually on the Island. The Young Gentlemen being placed in position . . . the word was given to fire. Both fired at once and . . . both were stung by the missiles . . . They came to the conclusion that there was something wrong . . . [and] they became exceedingly indignant, but their Friends succeeded in settling the matter between them. . . .

One afternoon while I was unpacking [to open a shop in Warsaw] there came a rap at the door and two well-dressed Gentlemen stepped in, saying they wanted to look at my Store and get acquainted with me. I welcomed them, and they asked . . . where I came from. I replied that I came from Lexington, but was born in New Jersey, and learned my business in Philadelphia. "Why you are a Yankee!" he said. I answered, "We do not account ourselves Yankees; we only recognize New England People by that name." He replied, "Jerseymen are the d—est, meanest kind of Yankees. There are too many d— Yankees here now, and we don't want any more of that breed." I asked him if he came into the Store to insult me, and he replied that I might put any construction on his remarks that I chose. I happened to be unpacking my Scales at the time, and taking a weight in each hand, I ordered him to get out of the store. His friend ran out quickly, but he gave me more impudence as he backed towards the door. I followed him up, menacing him with the weights, and keeping a sharp lookout for his Pistol, having learned well the Character of such Desperadoes; but he did not draw it, and as he backed out I slammed the door and locked it.

George Thurber (b. 1821?- d. 1890),
Providence, Rhode Island, 1841-1842

From a diary kept during a final year as an apprentice and the first year as a pharmacist and owner.

1841

January

5: . . . Had the pleasure of knowing practically the making of Pills of Colchicum and Sulphate of Iron, an all day job. Made great improvement in the method of pulverizing colchicum seeds, viz., grinding them in a mill—rather tough business at any rate.

7: . . . Left alone [in the shop] in the evening and amused myself with the Argand lamp.

14: . . . Cracked Gum Senegal all day.

15: . . . In the evening I went to Prof. Chase's lecture on Galvanism where I saw some experiments which I never saw before, such as the decomposition of water and of salts.

February

11: . . . Mr. Balch went to Boston. Mem.: The best way to make a small quantity of oxygen is to make it from oxide of manganese and sulphuric acid and heat it by a spirit lamp.

12: . . . Attended Prof. Chase's lecture in the evening. Subject: Chlorine, Bromine, Iodine & Fluorine. Having never seen any experiments in these subjects they were particularly interesting to me. . . . Mem.: Syrup of Sarsaparilla is too strong when made by the process of displacement [i.e., percolation].

19: . . . In the evening I attended the meeting of the chemical class at the Franklin Society's rooms, through the influence of my friend Mr. Owen Mason.

25: . . . [Aroused by the cry of "fire," worked at the pump with volunteer firemen, then] went down to the store and sat until daylight. We got along quite well through this first day of the absence of our Boss. Made gold leaf and quadrant electrometers.

March

3: . . . Last night I read an article on morphology. The speculation is very plausible in appearance, but perhaps it will not bear the

test of observation. Worked today upon the compound blow-pipe.

10: . . . Bleached sponges today. . . . Read Lindley's Botany in the evening.

17: . . . I gave a lecture on oxygen before the Society this evening. I prepared the gas from chlorate of potassa. My experiments all succeeded and some were very brilliant, particularly the burning of Iron and Phosphorous in Oxygen.

19: . . . Attended the chemical class in the evening. We made Muriatic Acid and Nitrous Oxide gases. . . . Moved Apiary.

April

4: . . . The Dr. returned today [Sunday]. Took a walk with him

. . . passed the most of the day in microscopic observation and obtained a tolerable knowledge of the [plant] tissues, etc. In the evening went to church and heard Mr. Balch preach upon the second death, in opposition to Miller—very well pleased.

18: . . . Sunday . . . In the forenoon I employed myself with tests for arsenic.

21: . . . In the evening went as usual to the Society meeting—best meeting that we have had for a long time. Question: "Which are more wonderful the works of nature or art?" Nature got it.

22: . . . Just two years ago today I entered this store as clerk. . . . Made Lenitive Electuary [a mild purgative].

27: . . . Pulverized Cantharides today, beautiful job!

29: . . . Mr. Balch went to New York today. I put up Godfrey's Cordial all day [with Tincture of Opium and Oil of Sassafras as key ingredients].

The leech jar disappeared slowly from dispensing counters during the nineteenth century, as therapeutic blood-letting fell out of favor. The proper care and application of leeches was part of a pharmacist's expertise. Pharmacist Zahn in St. Louis, for example, tells (p.85) of making the importation of leeches his specialty during the 1870s. (Photo courtesy of George Grider and the McDowell Apothecary Shop.)

May

4: . . . I made Syrup of Sarsaparilla today.

16: . . . Walked in the morning with Dr. C[hapin?] through the usual road. In the afternoon I walked solus on a botanizing expedition. Found a few flowers—some anemones, epigeas, etc. Passed the evening with Mrs. B and daughter.

23: . . . O.Ch. lent me his microscope. Amused myself with it in the afternoon.

28: . . . We made Emplastrum Picis Burgundicae [pitch plaster].

30: . . . Went to walk with the Dr. in Seikonk. Found quite a number of flowers. Passed the afternoon with the microscope—very well pleased.

June

3: . . . Finished the Envoy's [medicine] chest and began the Brunswick's.

5: . . . Finished up the whale ship's chest today, thank fortune.

23: . . . Dr. Maurun presented me with a plant of Popinac, a West Indian hedge shrub. Society meeting this evening. G.B. again rejected. Debate was on [universal male] suffrage.

28: . . . Sailed down the river this afternoon to the whale-ship Envoy, which sails tomorrow. . . . What a dismal place that forecastle must be to live in.

July

4: . . . Sunday, the glorious Fourth. Went to the grotto with Mr. M . . . Found some beautiful and rare plants, among them were Chimaphila, Convolvulaceae, and Asclepias.

7: . . . Pulverized 9 lbs. Cantharides—an all day job. . . . Moved into my new room.

8: . . . Made up the Blister Plaster today, 27 lb. Hope that it will last. . . . Mr. Balch has gone to Boston.

10: . . . The articles which M. B. bought in Boston were received today. Elisher hair brushes Whew! What next?

11: . . . Fine morning. Sunday. Walked with Dr. C. around by Moses Brown's and Gov. Flenner's. We found some flowers—scullcap, prunella, Lilium canadense, loose strife, &c.

13: Very warm. Made Unguentum Stramonii, an odoriferous job; also Succus spicatus con. nucae[?].

20: . . . Started this morning for Boston per R.R.. . . . Called on Mr. Joseph Burnett. . . . He is in Metcalf's, the "crack" apothecary store. . . . Saw [in Salem] the Drugstore of S. S. Harrison, maker of the Peristaltics.

23: . . . Took carriage for Winships Nurseries, etc. . . . in Brighton. . . . There were several varieties of passiflora. . . . Got some buds and flowers (P. quadrangularis), which we carried home safely; here were also a number of cacti. . . . After paying 75c for a poor dinner we adjourned to Cushing's celebrated garden, the finest in New England. . . . We then commenced our ride for home. . . . Having heard that Mr. Burnett had been hurt by the bursting of a soda water bottle, I called on him and found him doing well. Passed the evening at the Museum.

24: . . . Visited the conservatory and public garden. . . . Went to the Horticultural Society's exhibition room. . . . I next went to Metcalf's and by the politeness of Mr. Burnett I examined his apparatus for charging soda fountains.

26: . . . Plenty of business. Extractum Colocynthidis Compositum. Bought Bigelow's "Florula Bostoniensis."

August

14: . . . New prescription scales. Tomatoes getting ripe.

26: . . . Put up a prescription the dose of which contained 1/1024 part of a grain of corrosive sublimate—not a homeopathic prescription either. A pretty close approach to the infinitestinal [sic].

27: . . . Full of work. A large lot of glass ware arrived today. Dropped in at the suffrage meeting. . . . The singing was execrable. . . . What will happen?

September

2 . . . My 20th birthday. Twenty years old! . . . Mr. M[ason] gave me a piece of Slicornia, a beautiful marine plant from which soda is made.

24: . . . Dr. has gone to the land of notions. Began the [medicine] chests of the ship Ballance. . . . Mal de tete, accordingly retired early.

October

1: . . . Went to writing school for the last time.

9: . . . The birthday of John. . . . The dear soul gave me a most beautiful copy of the British poets, including Scott's Marmion, Lady of the Lake, etc.

12: . . . Confectio Sennae Comp. . . . Mr. M. has at last found the root of the Bean Vine. Hope he will be satisfied now.

22: . . . Quarter day. Been at Balch's two and a half years. Struck for another evening [off] in the week but 'twas no go.

25: . . . The English have given the Chinese a severe whipping [in the "Opium War"?], confound them. . . . Sent Burnett a Boullay's Instrument [for percolation?].

26: . . . Mr. Mason showed me a new and very delicate balance, which weighs from 1000 grains to 1/1000 of a grain.

27: . . . Distilled Ether Chlorini (U.H.M.).

November

13: . . . Made Aqua Destillata all day. Wet, tiresome work.

16: . . . The vapour of Iodine is very irritating to the eyes. Put up Godfrey's Cordial all day. The old boss is as fidgety as can be. What an ass.

24: . . . I bleached sponges today. Mem.: An inhalation of chlorine is "verry purtickerly" disagreeable.

30: . . . Wrote Burnett. There has also been quite a diabolical "scolcotoxicological" [anthelmintic] correspondence between Dr. C and my pompous self.

December

8: . . . Put up Solid Opodeldoc [a form of camphorated soap liniment]. . . . Listened to the reading by Mr. M. of a letter from Prof. Bailey on "Desmidiaceae."

18: . . . Digby has bought a pound of boneset candy for this slippery weather [i.e., Eupatorium as a cold remedy].

20: . . . Albert and myself pulverized 12 lb. Cantharides this afternoon! Unprecedented celerity! Feel quite used up after the exploit.

1842

January

1: . . . We had a great deal to do at the store today. . . . This page is written with ink made in one day by the process of peroxidation, which is a great saving of time.

7: . . . Dull in the store. Oh, the perplexities and doubts that attend one as soon as he thinks of [owning] business. They are almost enough to discourage anyone. Shall I or not?

11: . . . Very dull at the store. The old boss has gone to Boston. As "when the cat is away the mice will play," we had a very cozy time.

16: . . . Passed the forenoon at the store reading Bulwer's Paul Clifford—abominable style. . . . The afternoon was spent in the writing of and the revision of labels with the Dr.

20: . . . Told Mr. Balch that I was about to leave him. Never saw a man so much struck in my life. Dont want me to go on any acct. . . . Intention of taking J & myself into Co. Really I am in a dilemma.

28: . . . The old Boss is as complaisant as his nature will admit. . . . Passed the evening with Dr & L in apportioning our stock that is to be. It will be no little trouble to arrange matters.

30: . . . Passed the forenoon at the store in reading the [American] Journal of Pharmacy. What a deal of study our business requires and it seems to me the more I read the less do I feel that I know. . . . I am afraid that I shall have to forgo many pleasures on going into business, but I am resolved that no desire for gain shall ever overcome my attachment to my friends.

February

2: . . . Can't say that I have done much today except quiddle. But there now seems a pretty clear prospect of having a determination speedily, pro or con. . . . I think so much about the business that I am unfitted for anything else.

4: . . . No further light upon the store business. . . . Essayed for the first time upon Emulsio Amygdali communis.

17: . . . We are pretty well sure of the store at No. 79 Westminster now occupied by G. L. Heap, which we are to have by paying him the sum of $50.00 [rent].

19: . . . This day is to be remembered as the last of my apprenticeship at Balch's—almost three years have I been there, three years! It doesn't seem so long ago as that, when on my debut I timidly looked about at the "fixens" with wonderment. Oh, thought I, when shall I ever learn all those hard [drug] names. When shall I know to distinguish such a variety of articles! It seems but a very short time ago. But then when I consider how much I have learned in that time it seems rather longer. Indeed I have learned much. . . . It is hard work to break the chain of acquaintance and suddenly quit old associations. How one gets attached to inanimate things. Every galli pot seemed to wear a longer face; every bottle seemed to nod good bye, and when for the last time I struck the pestle, with which there are so many queer associations, the mortar seemed to ring out a stifled knell-like adieu.

21: . . . How queer I feel without an abiding place. We have passed the day in making preliminary enquiries and estimates. Haven't accomplished much as yet.

23: . . . Been pretty busy in running about hither and yon. Bought some glass ware. Made Rochelle Mixture and cut [powder] papers. . . . Passed the evening in putting up Rochelle powders.

25: . . . the Dr and myself went to an attorney and got spliced, in other words we signed the agreement of Company Partnership. Passed the afternoon putting up powders, which is a tedious job. . . . Mr. M read me his lecture upon Botany, comprising the Exogens and Endogens.

26: . . . Made out a long order for herbs from the Shakers.

28: . . . It seems really natural to get among the drugs again. All the forenoon pounding for, and preparing, tinctures. In the afternoon borrowed Balch's still (which he loaned with pretty good grace) and distilled water.

March

7: . . . The Dr. [Joshua Chapin] and myself went to Boston to purchase goods for our [new] store.

8: . . . The Dr. went home this morning to look after the carpenters, leaving the [rest of the buying] business with myself. . . . After breakfast, traded with Wm. Brown, a clean chap; Ashton, the fancy goods man, in whose store I saw many beautiful things; called on Henshaw, Ward & Co., . . . they do business up very genteelly. Traded with Bradford, &c, and then to dinner. Prof. [Benjamin] Silliman and son were in the omnibus.

9: . . . Stole a few moments from my business to visit Dr. [James] Jackson, to whom I had an introduction from Mr. Mason. His laboratory and office are in fine style. Gave his apparatus a passing look, but saw enough to make me wish to be among it. . . . Bought Oil of Condrieaux. . . . Called to say farewell to [friend] Burnett and drank [soda] to our success, and arrived at the cars just in time.

A rare glimpse of an American pharmacy about 1831, from an old stereotype made for the druggist Joseph T. Brown of Boston. At right, an exceptionally spacious and well-appointed dispensing area; at left, an early style of soda fountain. The wholesale arm of Brown's "Chemical Store" is emphasized by shipping cartons that the artist has placed in the foreground. (From the William H. Helfand Collection.)

14: . . . Today we began in earnest with the compounds. What with pounding drugs and sifting pulps I have been pretty busy. Dr. Wadsworth says that Troy weights won't do for this country.

15: . . . Quite busy in pounding and compounding. Received some pods of Cathartocarpus Fistulosa—queer things. . . . Passed the evening in making a sieve with Dr. Lou and Miss Rogers.

16: . . . Have been busy today in preparing Confectio Sennae, Syrupus Rhei, &c., and in garbling Colocynth, a bitter task.

21: . . . Have been very busy all day in carting drawers, lugging bottles, making [galenical] preparations. Wrote Burnett for [Solar] lamps.

28: . . . Our store has been resounding . . . with click of hammers tacking carpet down. We opened for the first time in the evening. Had a good many friends in to look about; some MDs. We did a fair little business considering it the first day.

30: . . . Business somewhat dull, but we have not been any ways idle. No apothecary ever need be. Our bright window continues to attract the attention of passers by. Ordered the soda fountain.

April

10: . . . Sunday . . . Staid at the store nearly all day, rather confining business.

19-21: . . . Made pine apple syrup [for the fountain]. . . . Put up Rochelle powders all the evening. . . . Our business has been good, profits $T.UO [pricing code]. . . . Our Soda Fountains came today, tall ones—regular steam boilers.

27: . . . Business decidedly dull.

30: . . . Business improves. . . . Our slab and fountain head were put up today and are admired by all for the chasteness of design and beauty of workmanship.

May

1: . . . Today all the drug stores close at half past ten and do not open for the remainder of the day. This gives great relief from busi-

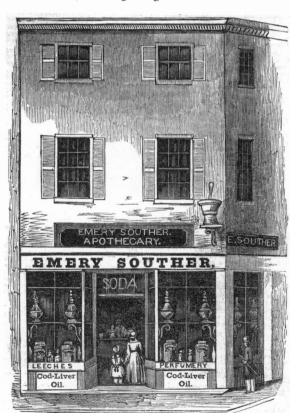

A Boston apothecary shop as it looked in the 1840s. Here apothecary Souther made a specialty of processing "purified Oil of the Cod-fish Livers," which he prepared daily for both retail and wholesale distribution. (Engraving from Emery Souther, A Treatise on the Medicinal Use of Cod-Liver Oil, *Boston, 1848.)*

ness, but I expect that it will not last. . . . In the afternoon . . . took a [botanizing] ramble in the grove back of the Quaker College and from there I went to that dear wild spot, the Grotto.

5: . . . Business a trifle better. We begin to sell some soda.

7: . . . It's a deal of work to keep our little store in anything like decent order. . . . There is so much [political] excitement that it injures all kinds of business. People look more after the Constitution of the state than they do after their own constitution. Thus ends the dullest week that we have had yet.

12: . . . The Chronicle gives us [Chapin & Thurber, Apothecaries] a bit of a puff, saying that our soda sparkles like the eyes of two belles he saw there (Mary A. and Mary W.).

17-19: . . . Closed the store at about 9 o'clock. My Uncle Henry

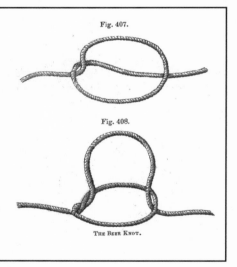

A pharmacy apprentice had to master the skill of perfectly packaging drugs, whatever the shape or size. Pharmacist John Moore remembers it well (p. 81). The drawing reproduced from the manual Practical Pharmacy *(1849), shows how to make secure a corked dispensing bottle by tying a "capping knot" over a bit of parchment paper. Knot tying, pill rolling, and powder-paper folding all required deftness and practice—as several memoirists attest.*

Fig. 407.

Fig. 408.

THE BEER KNOT.

and John Garitt and Tom went out to the arsenal to get guns. . . . Rose at a very early hour and went to look after my store, found it safe. I had supposed that the windows would have been broken. . . . The mayor has issued a request for all persons to close their places of business and take up arms for defence of the laws of the state. In accordance with which I closed and went to the Council chamber, got a gun and ammunition, and fell in with the volunteer citizens under the command of Col. Bill Blodget. . . . The Locofocos held a meeting in the park on Tuesday [—agitating for universal male suffrage, state re-apportionment, and other Constitutional reforms]. . . . Staid at the Cadets armory all night as a volunteer guard.

June

12: . . . Sunday. . . . After dinner I walked on the banks of the Moshashuck river as far as Capt. Coaks Cemetery, a pleasant place. Found there some fine specimens of Saracenia Purpurea, the first time I ever saw it in flower; also found our beautifully delicate, native columbine. . . . Confound that Chapin, I wish he would mind his own business.

17: . . . Exceedingly warm. Soda sells well. . . . Saw the Liriodendron tuliperferum in bloom for the first time—magnificent.

23: . . . This [patrol duty] deprives me of sleep . . . Opened store and breakfasted. . . . Went to drill in the afternoon.

25-30: . . . All the forces now in the city [of Providence] were ordered to meet this afternoon for review. We closed doors and went. . . . There was about 1700 men under arms and 11 cannon on the field. . . . The city and state are under martial law. . . . The streets are full of soldiery. Our streets have the appearance of a morning holiday, nearly all stores being closed. . . . The Cadets were driven to Pawtucket, where the Irish were in arms. . . . volunteers requested for Pawtucket. On our arrival the streets were filled with an abusive mob. . . . Was detailed to guard the state's prison at night. . . . Dr. Lewis P. Parlin, the suffrage Locofoco and homeopathic physician, has been arrested.

July

1: . . . Passed the forenoon in cleaning up. Business very good.

4: . . . Business except soda has been very dull. In the evening our store was thronged with the "fair sex," who were after summat [somewhat] to drink. I got really tired of it.

Evan Tyson Ellis, (b. 1826-d. 1913),
Philadelphia, Pennsylvania, 1840-1870

I can remember as a child a lot of mystical, urn-shaped jars on the top shelves marked "Confect.," "Theriac," "Confect. Damocratis," etc., as some of you saw at the recent [1902] American Pharmaceutical Association exhibition; but there never was such in my time [in the shop], for old things were discarded as new ones came into play; and when we left Chestnut Street in 1857, we placed an entire new up-to-date outfit on the shelves, and no doubt gave the old to some one starting out. . . .

In 1844 . . . having graduated from Haverford College I entered on apprenticeship and, also having graduated in the College of Pharmacy in 1847, I was in 1850 given an interest in the [family] business. . . . We were emerging from the retail to the wholesale, though for years there was more or less of the former done. . . . Charles Ellis & Co. [had entered] the market as regular manufacturing chemists. . . .

When sailing ship and packhorse brought a burlapped bale of crude drug from some exotic place, it could fire the imagination of a young druggist. This nineteenth-century shipment might have been gambir extract, opium cakes, or areca nuts—staple commodities of Johore on the Malaysian peninsula.

[During the Civil War] every old thing was saleable in the way of drugs. As members of the Society of Friends, we could not accept contracts for army supplies that were offered us, much to the amazement of the army people, . . . but after war had done its terrible work we could give to the relief association for the wounded, which we were glad to do. . . .

An agreeable feature of our business was the very pleasant personal relations we had with our customers and those with whom we had dealings. Our Boston friends, particularly appreciated reciprocal dealings, so that our preparations obtained quite a sale through New England.

Alpheus P. Sharp (b. 1824-d. 1909), Baltimore, Maryland, 1840s

Our Lecture course at the Maryland College of Pharmacy, 1841, was only one year of six months. Dr. David Stewart lectured on chemistry without using notes but followed Bache in the U. S. Dispensatory. He made his talks, for that is what they were, of little value, as he was a poor speaker with a bombastic style. He told us about copper sulphate, also a few other chemicals, and dwelt considerably on physics, his only piece of apparatus being a statical electric machine with which, after class, we amused ourselves beyond measure by taking *shocks*. . . . Dr. Rush Roberts lectured on Materia Medica, reading his lectures which closely followed Wood in the Dispensatory. Thomas G. Mackenzie [a Baltimore pharmacist] was the great moving spirit in establishing the College of Pharmacy. He gave us occasional talks in the absence of the regulars—lectures given in his little office . . . to a class of six young men [of whom three did graduate] and were successful. It was easy then, for we knew so little. . . . Robert H. Coleman . . . delivered the [Commencement] address, which was fine, he being a remarkable pharmacist teeming with useful advice from his individual experience.

In 1842, when 19 years old, I assisted Charles C. Caspari, then about 27, to open his drug store. He could not speak English and knew only the German method of running the business, in consequence of which it devolved upon me for quite a while to take absolute charge. I remained with him six years, becoming almost invaluable, and then I opened . . . my own store . . . taking along much of Mr. Caspari's trade, thus giving me a good business from the start. Six or seven years later I took into my store Louis Dohme, who scarcely could speak any English, but quickly picked it up to perfection.

Mr. Caspari was great on decoctions and infusions, and even brought over with him from Germany a Beinzan apparatus for preparing them. We also made in his store extract of hyoscyamus, getting as much product as the weight of [crude] drug taken. He knew all about chemical symbols and, no doubt, would have been a professor at the College but for his English.

Theodore R. Wardell (b. 1832), New York City, Georgia, &c., 1844-1865

An orphan at the age of twelve years, I entered the retail drug store of Allan P. Halleck & Co., at 149 Fulton Street, New York, a few doors from Broadway, north side, August 1st, 1844. My grandfather, James Wilson, a stove dealer and manufacturer, paid Dr. Halleck $1 a month to teach me the drug business. I was small for my age and stood on a box to properly use a mortar and pestle on the counter. Dr. Halleck and his partner, Mr. Stoddard, were kind hearted Quaker gentlemen and I rose rapidly in their esteem—and as a druggist. . . . In those days we bought our supplies of drugs mostly of Olcott & McKesson, wholesale druggists in Maiden lane. . . . In the latter part of the forties I came South, to Richmond, Va. [and later practiced in Galveston, Tex. and Savanna, Ga.]. In 1858 I began business in this city (Bainbridge, Ga.) and am still [in 1904] at work every day in the week.

I was a Confederate soldier three years, and when the war closed I had charge of the purveyor's department for furnishing medical and hospital supplies for eastern and middle Florida for the Confederate forces. . . . My three years in the war were not lost to me, for I was compelled by reason of the blockade to manufacture to fill the wants of the army in the field. I saw tight times to fill requisitions for some things: At one time we used tupelo gum tree roots in making corks. I also found dogwood bark made a fair black ink. Bottles were scarce and I gathered them up from the towns and plantations.

I have been through three epidemics of yellow fever and stood in my place behind the counter the whole time, except in part of one when I had the fever, but was again behind the counter in three weeks.

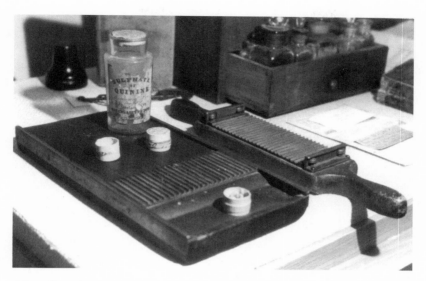

The pill machine was pronounced "an indispensable article for every druggist" by the middle years of the nineteenth century, when these artifacts were in use. A pill mass containing the prescribed amount of the quinine sulphate was rolled out on the flat surface of the machine as a pencil-shaped "pill pipe." The pharmacist laid the pipe crosswise on the metal grooves; and then rolled the matching grooved plate (with handles) back and forth to cut the pill mass into dosage units and round them into pill form—to be perfected, when necessary, by rolling each pill briefly between a practiced thumb and forefinger. Round cardboard pill boxes were used for dispensing, as shown.

Christian Frederick G. Meyer (b. 1830), Fort Wayne, Indiana, and St. Louis, Missouri, 1848-c.1860s

My brother, William, and I started on the 25th of September, 1847, from Bremen, on the sailing vessel, "Swanton." After seven weeks, and three days, we arrived at New Orleans. . . . From New Orleans we went by boat to Cincinnati, which took nearly two weeks. At Cincinnati, I took a canal boat to go further north, but after a day and a night the canal became covered with ice, and, as I wanted to go to a place in Indiana where I had a sister living, I was obliged to walk afoot the balance of the way. . . . In February, 1848, I went to the nearest town, Fort Wayne, Indiana. . . . One day, when looking around and

Probably the earliest known photograph of an American pharmacist at work.
Behind the dispensing counter, in the mid-19th century, a practitioner has at
hand three resources essential to all the practitioners represented in Drugstore
Memories: *mortar-and-pestle, counter balance, and dispensatory. (Daguerreotype*
from the Greg French Collection, as reproduced in: M. A. Foresta and J. Wood,
Secrets of the Dark Chamber: The Art of the American Daguerreotype.
Washington, DC: National Museum of American Art, Smithsonian, 1995.)

not knowing where to go [for a job], a gentleman . . . took me into a
[drug] store and calling the proprietor (whose name was H. B. Reed,
by his given name), he said, "This boy wants work." The first order
this Druggist gave me was to make a fire in a stove—the beginning of
my career in the Drug Business. I remained till 1852 when I started
on my own account. . . .

The [wholesale and retail drug] business I am engaged in [as
Meyer & Brother] is very interesting in many respects (but every man
finds his business interesting if he loves it). We deal in goods that are
produced and gathered in all parts of the world. They are manifold in
their character, being of the Mineral, Vegetable, and Animal Kingdoms. They are gathered from the seas, on the mountains, in the exotic and the Arctic countries. . . . We order goods by cable from Ja-
pan, from China, India, Asia and Oceanica. We have orders from
Europe, from the West Indies, Australia and many other foreign lands.

C. V. Emich (b. 1833), Baltimore, Maryland, 1848-1851

I entered the business as an apprentice in February, 1848 and am still pegging away, sometimes tempted to complain at the changes. . . . At that time, 1848, the drug business in Baltimore was just freeing itself from the oil, paint and glass business, and by 1850 this was fully accomplished.

During this time [the apprentice] was called upon for the development of patience and muscle by the use of the mortar and pestle; for let it be understood that the pharmacist or druggist of that day did not have the supply of powdered and ground drugs to aid him that he now has. It was in the latter part of 1849 that Messrs. Haskell, Merrick and Ball, of New York, introduced to the profession a series of powders, well prepared, put up in 1 pound bottles in green paper cases that were hailed as a decided boon to the afflicted ones, weary of patience and practice. . . .

In those days there were but few books to be had. . . . Of chemistry, Johnston's and Turner's and Kane's chemistry were the ones placed in the young man's hands, if the proprietor troubled himself at all about it. Wood and Bache's Dispensatory, Faraday's Chemical Manipulations, and later Campbell Morfit's work were the principal ones to be found. Mohr and Redwood's Pharmacy, edited and revised by Mr. Wm. Procter . . . was a revelation to me, nor have I forgotten the value of [Edward] Turner's chemistry in the multitude of compounds described, which has stood me in good stead during my trials and tribulations in the business.

William T. Wenzell (b. 1829-d. 1913), St. Louis, Missouri, and La Crosse, Wisconsin, c.1850-1867

At the expiration of my apprenticeship [as a bookbinder] I concluded to adopt pharmacy as my future profession and obtained a position in a small retail drugstore in the outskirts of St. Louis. The tutor in the store was a German, Doctor Koch, who was a character "sui generis" of a German student. His long-stemmed "Weichsel" [cherrywood] pipe seemed to be his only solace; and while filling the back room of the pharmacy with its dense fumes, he would relate the escapades and duels of his university life [in Germany]. Under his instruction I prepared nearly all of the elementary gases, made gun-cotton, which had just been discovered by Schoenbein, reduced ferric oxide by hydrogen, extracted Caffein from raw coffee, prepared a number of salts, and experimented in photography. . . . Under the guidance of this thorough German "Apotheker" I obtained within a year enough Knowledge to take charge of a larger store in a principal street.

Becoming restive, with a desire to see more of the world, I gave up my position to visit other cities, taking positions as assistant in New Orleans and Panama City, &c, finally coming to Philadelphia to attend the College of Pharmacy. I took charge of a small physician's drugstore in West Philadelphia, while attending the evening lectures of the College and, after the regular two years course, graduated in 1855, with William Procter Jr., Robert Bridges, and Dr. [Robert P.] Thomas as my professors. Thesis [was on the proximate analysis of tubers of] Corydalis formosa.

In the fall I accepted a call to return to the West, from the firm of Samuel D. Hastings & Co., La Crosse, Wisconsin, then merely a trading post of perhaps 300 inhabitants. Mr. Hastings carried on a general merchandise store, [where I was] to take charge of the drug department. I lived in La Crosse twelve years, six years as [prescription] clerk and six years as proprietor. I [had] opened a drugstore under the name of Wenzell and Moller, which was the beginning of my prosperity. . . . But in 1867 I disposed of my business and emigrated to this city (San Francisco) . . . for a better and more congenial climate.

John A. Dadd (b. 1829-d. 1895), Milwaukee, Wisconsin, 1850-c.1885

I came to Milwaukee in the year 1850 from London, England, [after] serving as an apprentice to my elder brother for three and one-half years, and acting as an assistant to a practicing surgeon and apothecary a year and a half or more. I anticipated finding, on coming to the far west [i.e., to Wisconsin], a society in a crude and undeveloped condition, expecting to see nothing but block houses and Indians camping and moving around; but contrary to my expectation found streets laid out in fairly good shape, some brick buildings three stories in height. . . . The population, I believe was from 8,000 to 10,000.

I landed from one of the many lake steamers that plied between Buffalo, Milwaukee and Chicago, then the only means of reaching these two latter cities, as railroads were not then built so far west. I obtained a situation with the firm of Hatch & Patterson, Druggists. . . . Mr. Hatch was from Vermont, where he learned the drug business. Mr. Patterson was from Pennsylvania, where he had followed the occupation of a tanner. It struck me as somewhat singular that a person who not been educated to the drug business should be following the same, but I soon became accustomed to this condition of things, finding it common for many to engage in all kinds of business with which

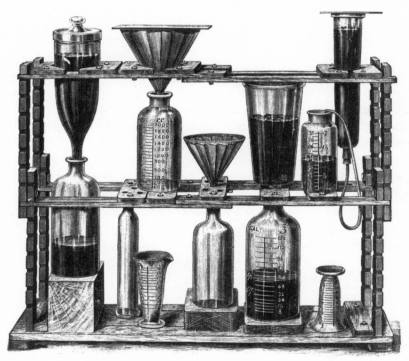

This percolation rack displays several variants of the basic method, which displaced maceration during the course of the nineteenth century as the preferred method for extracting the active principles of botanical drugs. Although developed in Europe, percolation underwent improvements in the hands of American pharmacists (notably 1845-75), and eventually was viewed as one of the most important pharmaceutical developments of the century.

they had not the slightest acquaintance . . ., but I have yet to meet such a man who in later life has been much of a success in our calling.

The drug business in those days [the 1850s] consisted of a most varied stock, comprising groceries, paints, oils, glass, and in some cases books and jewelry. . . . Labor was not divided into departments: you were obliged to act as porter, errand boy and prescription clerk, clean windows, trim oil lamps, . . . sweep the store, pack goods for shipping, sleep among the barrels of sugar, chests of tea and boxes of drugs; in fact, make yourself generally useful, measuring molasses, counting candles, putting up soap, and compounding a prescription when required.

Dispensing was not done with that nicety that had been thoroughly inculcated into me [in England], and I was surprised to see quinine dumped into a bottle, a little dilute or aromatic sulphuric acid added, shaken up, other ingredients added without measurement, corked and labeled. . . . Packages were put up without particular regard to the shape or style, in many cases without any selection as to the paper. I . . . preferred to compound medicines in a proper manner and to put up a good looking package. I found after a while that I was commended for it. . . .

The manufacturing department, as might be expected was somewhat crude in its methods; the weights employed were avoirdupois; the menstruum employed in which drugs were macerated for tinctures was common whisky, instead of dilute alcohol, and sugar for syrups was not the most refined kind. Many of the medicaments were strange to me, not being in the British Pharmacopoeia. Aromatic Syrup of Rhubarb was one; and a preparation of capsicum and myrrh called Hot Drops was another. Another Thompsonian remedy called Composition—a compound of bayberry, capsicum, ginger and cloves in powdered form—is still in vogue [1890s]. Hiera Picra, or Powdered Aloes and Canella, was new to me; and Shaker herbs and roots were to me quite a novelty. I soon learned their uses as they were then, as now, in demand constantly.

I was particularly impressed with the wide difference in the doses of calomel [mercurous chloride] and quinine, as used in England. There the largest dose of calomel was 5 grains; here I found it frequently exhibited in 10, 15, and sometimes 30 grains. . . . Dr. Blanchard told me that when the Illinois canal was being excavated it was common to take a teaspoon filled half with calomel and the other half quinine, to give as a dose to counteract the effects of malaria. I was also surprised with the freedom with which poisons were sold, no particular supervision being kept. There were no strictly retail [drug] stores; they were wholesale and retail combined. . . . The first exclusively retail store was opened by I. N. Morton, on Wisconsin street, about the years 1858 to 1860, as nearly as I can recollect.

Among the most prominent patent or proprietary medicines, sold principally on commission, were Townsend's, Sand's and Bristol's sarsaparilla, Ayers' and Joujuc's medicines, Brandreth's and Moffatt's pills, Osgood's Cholagogue for ague. Davis' Pain Killer was introduced about this time, also Extract of Witch Hazel. As years have rolled on, this incubus upon our following has developed in a wondrous degree, until now it seems almost as if the stock of those dealing in drugs was composed mostly of them [the proprietary medicines]. . . .

We cannot, as formerly, obtain them on commission, but must invest our capital in them by purchase. This is brought about by the enormous amount of advertising [by the manufacturers] in newspapers, almanacs, etc., creating a demand by the public we cannot refuse to meet, however much we may be opposed in principle. This evil will require time, thought and ability to overcome and, I must add, much patience. The majority [of such products] are a monstrous imposition on the public. But I believe, in a measure, it can be curtailed and regulated by wise and efficient legislation, and such legislation should be sought. . . . It was not until 1876 that any legislation in regard to the competency of a pharmacist or regulating pharmacy was in force, . . . and its provisions applied solely to the city of Milwaukee.

M. Joseph Muth (b. 1837-d. 1898), Baltimore, Maryland, c.1851-1880

When I, a lad of thirteen, entered the wholesale drug house of Poplein and Thomsen, in 1851, crude drugs of vegetable origin and dyestuffs were our leading commercial articles. Making fires, sweeping floors and weighing out drugs, but never wrapping or labeling them, were my chief duties. I continued with the firm and its direct successors . . . until 1884, when Muth Brothers was formed. . . .

Chemicals were few in those days and alkaloids scarcely in any demand, but Rochelle and Epsom salts were quite popular—Baltimore being headquarters for the latter, and so listed in chemical and trade reports. Adjacent Anne Arundel County furnished magnesium clay of high grade, from which the salt was manufactured extensively in our city. Only a few patent medicines were popular: Swain's Panacea, Hawks' Panacea, Brandreth's Pills and Wright's Pills being the four leaders. The most accredited retail store at that early period was Coleman and Rogers . . . whose semiannual bills with us averaged $150, from which the profits must have been quite a thousand dollars. They were patronized by our best and wealthiest families, stood high personally, lived well, drove fast horses and were looked upon by the trade in every respect as *bon ton*. . . .

In the 50s and 60s the powdering of drugs involved much labor for retail and wholesale druggists, as it had to be done by hand, there being no specific machinery. Our two large mortars were kept in continuous service—one of iron, two feet high, 1-1/2 feet in diameter, 3-4 gallon capacity, with a solid iron pestle, four feet long and 1 inch in diameter and enlarged at the lower end to 3 or 4 inches. It was employed chiefly in reducing ergot, rhubarb, bayberry, etc., using mostly a vertical motion. The other mortar was marble, broad and shallow, the bowl 3-4 gallon capacity—the lower portion of the pestle being marble—conical shape, rounded base, 6-8 inches in length and breadth, joined to a long wooden rod whose upper end passed through a hole in the ceiling. The operator simply gave the pestle a swinging rotary motion, when by contusion or trituration substances like acacia, borax, ammonium chloride, etc., could readily be reduced. The first drug mill, Spencer-Thomas pattern, was used here in 1865, but only for bruising, not powdering. . . .

Business Decadence.—The decadence of the drug business in our city has been due to (1) Jealousies and misunderstandings among our retail druggists, for as early as 1855 at a called meeting . . . a uniform price list was submitted and signed. . . . [but] in a short time all were violating the letter of the schedule, which soon led to disturbed confidence—a general distrust that has not decreased with the years. . . . (2) Department stores have contributed a share of injury to the retail drug business. . . . As an offset to this innovation we strongly advised pharmacists to carry two grades, *cheap* and *expensive*, of all articles that shared in price cutting, thereby giving patrons a choice according to price.

I think the advent of the "drummer," always so keen and aggressive toward selling, gave the initial impetus to "cut rates". . . . William H. Read gave us, in 1862, our first "cut rate" store of druggists' sundries and supplies. . . . His store worried our druggists considerably, causing some to advise meeting his prices, and the majority to endorse a regular campaign toward convincing the public *that all accredited drug store articles sold anywhere at irregular rates were not genuine but spurious.* The result was that many persons thereafter patronized only the drug stores which maintained standard prices. . . .

Personal Decadence.—I attribute the weakening of our personnel to the lower attraction the drugstore now offers. Formerly, in the absence of [the big] manufacturing establishments, it involved considerable technical experience and interesting chemical processes that required a high order of intelligence and training. This made for a social recognition which appealed strongly to quite a few young men with laudable birth and advantages. Stores were less numerous, sales and profits larger, while salaries seldom ranged lower than a thousand dollars per annum—quite sufficient to prevent unrest and stimulate planning to start one's own business.

James Winchell Forbes (1837-c.1912), Lansingburgh, New York; San Francisco, Mud Springs, and Sacramento, California, 1853-1879

I returned to Lansingburgh, and in a few days accepted a position in a drugstore, . . . my first real entry into the practical drug business. In a few months Levi Hanford, my employer, . . . sold out to a man named Rogers, who came from New York City. Rogers at once transformed the store into a manufacturing plant for Seidlitz powders, flavoring extracts, and a more or less base imitation of "Sozodont". . . . I was kept busy cutting vanilla beans with a jack knife, pound after pound, not to speak of tonguas [tonka beans]. . . . We made our extract by digesting the bean with water and a little sal tartar, using alcohol only as a preservative. We also used to make genuine(?) Harlaam Oil, Hill's Balsam of Honey, Steer's Opodeldoc, Whiting's Liquid Opodeldoc, Bateman's Drops, and a lot of other things that are now [in 1910] known only to the oldest inhabitant. . . .

We had a twenty-gallon copper still with a goose neck capital (low heads were not then used), a forty-gallon copper kettle, and a whole army of Mohr, Redwood and Procter's contraptions [as described in their *Practical Pharmacy* . . .]. I remember the old shelf ware and the painted labels—about a third of a circle of gold leaf for the background and black lettering . . . The bottles were of German blown ware—very far from being uniform either in shape or capacity. . . .

My knowledge of drugs was somewhat to the hither side of elementary, and I was rather awed by the [labeled] bottles, such as Pulvis Stannum, and Oculis Cancrorum. One of my first sales was a "sixpence" worth of Mucuna Pruriens [a vermifuge]. . . . The array of patent medicines was a meagre one, and consisted primarily of the "genuine" English proprietaries made by my great uncle in his wholesale store, three miles down the Hudson river.

In the cellar we had a huge iron mortar, and one of marble, big enough to drown a dog in. My initiatory exercise, the day I went to work, was powdering a pound of Aloes; I also powdered Ipecac, made Unguentum Hydrargyri (strengthened with lampblack), and something I supposed would become Unguentum Hydrargyrum Nitratis. I know positively that I made an awful mess. . . . According to the most improved style of autobiography, I should chronicle as a fact that I made rapid progress in the art and science of pharmacy, but truth compels me to say that I did nothing of the kind.

[After arriving in San Francisco in 1859, I first worked in a steam lard-oil factory, then] learned that a boy was wanted at the drug store . . . of a Dr. Taylor, . . . who cooked his meals in the back room of the store and was very peculiar. . . . My wages were to be fifty dollars a month. This seemed to be just fifty more than I had been getting and was a pretty solid honorarium. . . . I was expected to be at the store at seven a.m., sweep out, etc., and get things ready for business. When I recalled my Lansingburgh experience, such as getting up at five a.m., I felt as if I had coralled a Sybaritic job. . . . After the chores of Monday morning were done, and Doctor Taylor had finished his morning shave, he sat down and we had a talk. He inquired into my past life and then pointed out the fact that I was still young and had my future in my own hands. "There is a great field for really good druggists in this country," he said, "and my advice to you is to study, not wildly as you have been doing, but go through a regular course

with the Dispensatory, and in few years you can fix your own wages."
I afterwards learned that the poor old man had heard of the Pharmacopoeia but had never seen a copy of it. . . .

About that time fluid extracts began to appear in the market,
and I got deeply interested in them, but had no idea of either menstr-
uums or processes. Before I got on the right track, I tried to make
Fluid Extract of Columba by boiling the root in water, and one may
imagine the mess. The Doctor knew even less than I did about such
things.

I staid with Doctor Taylor until early in the Fall, then thought
that I was worth more than a half century every thirty days. . . . The
owner disagreed with me. There were no [other drugstore] openings in
San Francisco. So I took the boat for Sacramento the next Monday
night. . . . [There I was employed by R. H. McDonald & Company.]
Of all the drugstores that I had seen, or have seen since, that one was
the oddest. . . .

When I asked Jonnie [a fellow employee] about percolators, he
told me that they made everything by maceration. This was joyful
news, as I reasoned that if they were farther behind the times than
Doctor Taylor, who had learned the business with Noah, I could soon
catch up with them. I worked diligently and in a few weeks had
ground all my drugs and had my bottles full and macerating while I
slept. . . . We made things in quantity and, for such articles as
Tinctura Gentianae Composita, my macerating vessels were five and
ten gallon kegs, with a cedar faucet at the bottom.

. . . The store opened at 5:30 a.m. to catch the teamsters' trade,
as the wagon trains usually got out of town early and were well on
their way by the time the sun got hot. What was put onto the front
end of the day was taken off the back end, as there was little evening
business; 7:30 was cash counting time. I staid with Mr. McDonald
about five months, as by that time had got the stock in good shape, in
fact had worked myself out of a job. . . . When the work petered out
the boss gave me a letter of recommendation to one of his best country customers, located in Mud Springs near Placerville. . . .

I found this place very congenial, and had plenty of time for
study. The owner was a Doctor Hinman, and the rumor ran that he
had started out as a horse doctor and worked his way up to human be-
ings. . . . While I was in Mud Springs I became interested in Salicylic

Acid, and made some from Oil of Wintergreen. I made a number of
Valerianates, . . . Butyric Acid and Oxalic Acid (from molasses). . . .
Castor Oil was the official axle grease, and every teamster carried a
half gallon tin can with a long oiling spout, . . . and it would
sometimes happen that five or six [freight] "schooners" with their
trailers would stop in front of the store at one time [for castor oil].
. . . "Mud" was the center of considerable excitement in copper
mining and I had a great deal of assaying to do. . . . Bob White [a
Placerville competitor] charged ten dollars for an assay of copper
ore no matter what the result was. I managed in a different way. If
the result was good, I would take my pay in the shape of interest
in the mine, but if there was little copper, I exacted the sawbuck [a
ten-dollar bill]. . . . But natural conditions in the shape of clouds
of alkali dust finally disgusted me with "Mud" and I determined
to leave. . . . [When] I heard that Jim Doherty of Sacramento
wanted a clerk, . . . I took the stagecoach for Sacramento.

Doherty was a graduate of the Dublin College of Pharmacy, . . .
the first real pharmacist I had met, and I set to work in earnest. He
disabused me of the idea that [George] Wood & [Franklin] Bache had
gathered [in the U.S. Dispensatory] all the knowledge of pharmacy
that was floating about, and he showed me copies of both the Dublin
and the Edinburgh Dispensatories, [F. L. M.] Dorvault's L'officine, the
Pharmacopoeia Borussica, and such a host of other works. . . .
Doherty took many journals and among them was the Pharmaceutical
Journal, published in England. An account of a preparation invented
by Schacht was very interesting to me. He called it "Liquor Bismuthi,"
and I made some and put it before our prescription-writing contin-
gent, which took very kindly to it. . . . I was still with Doherty when
the great flood came, and for three days we both worked in water
nearly up to our waists, our place being the only one in Sacramento
that was not totally disabled. . . .

Doherty's [alcoholic] sprees began to get closer and closer together, [and he became] abusive to every one. I saw that it was no
place for a man who loves peace and quietness, and wrote to a friend
in San Francisco that I was ready to make a change.

On my arrival in San Francisco [at about age 31], I was sent out
to the branch store at the corner of Third and Howard streets, then
under the management of Charlie Biedermann, . . . He had learned

the drug business in Germany, and France, was with the French army in Algiers as a pharmacien, and had traveled all through Mexico. His wife was a beautiful Mexican woman. . . .

Out of Biedermann's Gallic experience and my Yankee inventiveness we evolved [a perfume,] a good seller for not only our store but for the main one on Montgomery street. . . . After a time I had to make the preparations, not only for our own trade, but for the other stores. . . . The world went very well for me then, but good luck, like love, never runs far without a snag, and I struck mine in due time. Charlie was cross and I know I was; so hearing of a vacancy in Oroville, Butte County, I applied for the place and got it.

Oroville was a place that *was*. The glory of its mines had departed, leaving but a few Chinamen to work over the exhausted placer mines. . . . [So I was soon in San Francisco again.] I had not been in the store an hour before I had sized up the force. I was the manager, a fact that was not yet apparent to Simon the clerk and Owens the porter. As for the nominal owner [the "irascible" Dr. Parkhurst], he was a fifth wheel whose ultimate mission was to run [the business] into the ditch.

Yet, everything was going smoothly, when one day Ben Thayer walked into the store with Billy Bryan and paralyzed me by announcing that Billy had bought the store. Now I knew Billy's methods, and . . . his was the first chain of drug stores that I had ever known. Such a thing struck me as incompatible with the spirit of the drug business, and I could see no great things for Forbes in the future. . . .

I kept my cello and fiddle at the store, and after closing time each night I scraped acquaintance with such music as I could master. I wrote a mass for a Catholic church whose organist was a personal friend. He was so well pleased with it, and the fathers also, that he asked me to rewrite it with full chorus and orchestra parts for use at St. Mary's. Another friend, Charlie Capp of *The Golden Era*, who had published a number of my short stories, . . . said that there was more money in story writing than in musical composition and, if I would set my head in that direction, I could make a name for myself. . . .

Moving day came [c. 1872], and the familiar store fixtures were taken apart to be erected in the new home. The store was on the corner, and had a very imposing front, the entrance being between two massive columns. . . . The laboratory was in the cellar, very large and well lighted . . . Our opening was on the evening that the first train was run on the Central Pacific road, and this train came to a stop in front of our store, Ben, Charlie and I being out front to greet it. . . .

With Thayer's pull with physicians, we could not do aught but jump right into a good business; and if I remember correctly, our receipts on opening day were about one hundred and fifty dollars in cash, and a goodly amount of book accounts . . . After a time, the strain of management began to tell on Biedermann, and he went back to Wakelee, and I was placed in charge, not only of the laboratory, but the entire inside business. Doctor Letterman was coroner, and all the analytical work came to me. . . . As to some of the doctors' prescriptions, I will say that charity covers a multitude of sins. . . .

Without the slightest warning, I was taken down with rheumatism, and it was six weeks before I was able to take my place again. . . . Finally I had to give up. . . . I left the Grand Hotel [store], and for some weeks luxuriated in irresponsibility. While I was thus industriously doing nothing, Jimmie Steele proposed that I should go to work in his [drugstore's] laboratory. I accepted, and took up the harness again, at a salary of seventy-five dollars a month, but I had no responsibilities to speak of. I had no idea what was going on until I was elected Secretary of the [California Pharmaceutical] Society and Jimmie resigned the Secretaryship of the Board of Pharmacy in my favor. Jimmie Steele had long nursed the idea of organizing a California College of Pharmacy in San Francisco, and [by 1873] I was also officiating as Secretary of the [new] College and was the professor of pharmacy. . . .

[However,] I could see that a mistake had been made, and that the combination salary of all my official positions could not be made large enough to turn the [financial] tide. . . . I resigned from all my positions at once, sold my furniture for what I could get, and with the proceeds sent my wife home to [her family in] Kansas. . . .

[After further misfortunes in Nevada, California, and Kansas, and a serious bout with tertian fever], I was a new man,. . . . but, despite a very cordial reception in St. Louis, I got no glad tidings of a situation in a drug store, and that night [brother] George and I took the train for Cincinnati. . . . I had practically become a nomad . . . and if the "wanderlust" was not strong enough to move me at sufficiently short intervals to prevent my becoming placebound, circumstances always took charge of my business and moved me. . . . [But] my arrival in Cincinnati [in 1879] was the turning point in my life.

John F. Hancock (b. 1834-d. 1909), Baltimore, Maryland, 1854-1867

I was nineteen years old and uncertain what to do. . . . A relative advised me to seek the position of teacher . . . but in the meantime [1854] Dr. J. L. Large in Baltimore offered me a position in his pharmacy . . . conducted in connection with his medical practice. . . . Everything was strange to me. I often think of the horrible odors of drugs in my early experience and the still more repulsive tastes, except that of licorice root. There was not a hydrant in the shop; therefore it was my duty to go with a bucket across the street to fetch water to wash the pharmacy utensils.

My contract with Dr. Large (which was verbal) was to remain with him for four years at a salary of twenty-five dollars for the first six months, with a gradual increase which brought it to eight hundred dollars for the period of four years, with table board in his home and to sleep in a room over the store. In 1855 Dr. Large . . . sold his pharmacy to Dr. Edmund Landis, another physician with a large practice . . . and to my surprise he proposed a partnership—the result being the firm of Landis & Hancock.

We employed Mr. [William] Taylor, a graduate of the Philadelphia College of Pharmacy, who had good store training and was invaluable to us, as my experience was extremely limited. Of especial value to me as a teacher, he mapped out a course of study and gave me practical lessons in manipulation. When Dr. Landis decided to sell his interest in October, 1855, I bought his share of the business and established the pharmacy of J. F. Hancock. The withdrawal of Dr. Landis, whose prescriptions had been a great help, caused sales to decline. Other physicians were prejudiced against my pharmacy, because of my limited experience and the connection of the two doctors who had owned it. . . . The next two years I attended the full course of lectures [at the Maryland College of Pharmacy, part-time] and was graduated in 1860. This gave me a foundation on which to build, and my hard experience made me wiser and better qualified. . . . I naturally desired to gain the confidence and respect of physicians. . . . I never by word of mouth solicited the patronage of a physician or a family, or endeavored unduly to induce the patrons of other pharmacists to deal with me. . . .

Business steadily improved and in 1866 I leased the building on the southeast corner of Baltimore and Caroline streets, diagonally across from the old shop. . . . The rear room was fitted up for prescription work, with a central semi-circle of shelves for small bottles, containing duplications from the large shop bottles in the front room. . . . The prescription counter was placed in full view of those in the front room, but sufficiently retired to avoid conversation while prescriptions were being compounded. All prescription poisons were kept in a dark case under lock and key: The laboratory was in the room used as a kitchen by [the former owner] Dr. Eareckson. . . . The more reputable patent medicines were in stock, but not placed in the sight of customers. Those made by irresponsible persons or quacks were not sold. . . . The practical character of this old pharmacy is endorsed by the present owner, Mr. W. F. Threde [1906]. . . . Asked why he had not remodeled the pharmacy according to up-to-date ideas, his reply was: "As a pharmacy it is up to date; I do not wish a department store."

Joseph L. Lemberger (b. about 1835-d. 1927), Philadelphia and Lebanon, Pennsylvania, 1850s-1916

When [I] first felt a desire to learn the drug business the *only way open* was to become an apprentice. The advertisement read: "*Wanted.*—An Apprentice to learn the Drug Business. Address P. Chemist, Ledger Office, Phila." This advertisement was answered and with my father's aid I found the way to the store in Philadelphia.

At my age, less than 14 year, the transaction involved submission to being bound by indenture for a term of six years and seventeen days. . . . I was put through a rather unpromising examination of a somewhat physical character. I overheard the remark made to my father. "He's a little fellow, I wanted a taller boy," and my father's reply, "You know, doctor, the most valuable goods come in small packages." . . . The next query was addressed to me, "You are from the country, do you speak German?" . . . A German doctor's prescription, just presented, was handed to me to translate the directions. I had no difficulty, . . . and after testing my ability to handle the heavy wood slides that protected the glass in the doors, a regular duty when closing shop at night (indicating that I had some muscle), I was passed on favorably as an applicant.

With my father at my side helping me to determine the subject I willingly submitted to severance from the home family ties, and enter the family and service of a stranger and new master thereafter, until I would become of age, 21 years. The papers were prepared and duly signed and I became an indentured or bound apprentice, my compensation being board, washing, clothing and the full privileges and cost of the Philadelphia College of Pharmacy included. . . . I graduated with the class of 1854, two years before the expiration of my apprenticeship. . . .

The rules of the drug store. . . were posted in a prominent place, and I was informed that the closer attention paid to the requirement of said rules the more comfort would I find in the new position.

My first duty was to become well acquainted with my daily routine of work. . . . One of the rules [was] "Have a place for everything and everything in its place." . . . I was instructed to familiarize myself with names, taste, smell and color of all drugs, roots, herbs, tinctures, and all other preparations. This soon became an inspiring factor when washing and arranging the shelf bottles, especially as I was inclined to be inquisitive and wanted to familiarize myself with all that belonged to the business. . . .

I was early taught the values of the weights, and graduate measures, and knowledge and capacity from a drachm vial to gallon bottle and from the smallest tin box to the gallipots and jars. . . . Much care was taken to have me learn to make a neat package, and it soon became my duty to put up epsom salts, senna and manna, in 3 and 5 cent packages, to be ready on call; cut powder papers of various sizes for prescription use and for Seidlitz and Soda powder. In the early days I was allowed to be at the prescription case, read and study the prescriptions, and witness the compounding, and ere long was permitted to cut and roll the pills by hand and with the pill machine. The preceptor, or senior clerk prepared the [pill] mass. I had an ambition to do everything I saw others do and after my first year in the college of pharmacy I . . . was permitted to make the more simple preparations of the Pharmacopoeia. During my first and second year a senior clerk was employed; after that time I was considered qualified and, under the surveillance of my preceptor, to some extent to take charge of the store and make most of the preparations. . . .

The retail drug business of that period was vastly different from what it is today [1916], and it is not surprising to hear occasionally that we are losing our identity. Many things are sold in drug stores now, that were not thought of in that day. We generally kept what the customers wanted and in this particular store they sometimes wanted glass and putty and an occasional call for mixed paint, and I have a memory of a remarkable fact, that these articles were most frequently called for on a Sunday morning. . . . We had mixed white lead as a base and with the aid of chromes, yellow and green, Prussian blue, vermilion, lamp black, we were able to accommodate such calls. There were no sidelines such as a soda water and sandwich counter, cigars and tobacco, confectionery, wash rags, cheap watches, cutlery, safety razors and chewing gum. We did sell good toilet soap . . . home made cologne water . . . a few French extracts for the handkerchief, and we made a specialty of genuine chamois skins and sponges.

[I] was messenger boy and enjoyed the outing when we had a call for something "just out of". . . . No bus or trolley cars then; and the occasional omnibuses were not for the accommodation of the drug apprentice; it was economy to walk; the bicycle was not in use then either. . . . I want to emphasize the fact that the drug store of that day

A mortar and pestle was used daily and often when preparing prescriptions or stock quantities of dosage forms, such as powders, pills, emulsions, or mixtures. Several types and sizes of mortars were required, especially before ground and powdered crude drugs became commercially available. Three of the seven styles offered in the McKesson and Robbins catalogue of 1883 were (l. to r.) an iron contusion mortar, an iron mortar for comminuting or mixing botanicals and chemicals, and a Wedgwood mortar (a hard porcelain) for trituration.

was what the patrons expected it to be—a place to get the medicines
they needed: whether three cents' worth of epsom salts to the family
receipt for cough syrup or the doctor's prescription. We did compound prescriptions with care, as the sign on the side of house indicated, and we made all our own preparations, some solid extracts,
fluidextracts, tinctures, in the good old way, by percolation. The iron
mortar and pestle was in practical use, now seldom seen. . . . We had
no drug millers at that time to prepare the powdered or granulated
drugs. . . . If it was the tincture of rhubarb, aloes, cinchona, columbo,
or any other bitter or aromatic drug, we got busy with the mill or
mortar and, with the aid of our bolting cloth or wire sieve, made what
we wanted, and we did it skillfully and cheerfully, of course. . . . Your
historian well remembers his aversion to aloes . . . and sometimes expressed with harmless expletives his feelings, when aloes had to be
powdered and sieved to make tinctures of aloes and myrrh or *Hiera
Picra*, all of which were popular remedies in that day.

This apprentice had an *extra* experience that I venture to affirm
few others had. My preceptor was a mechanical genius, as well as a
practicing physician and pharmacist. As a sideline he had orders for articulated human skeletons. The bones were obtained from the University dissecting department. . . . When finished, they . . . were no
doubt used in a secret society initiation ceremony. . . .

We also had another innovation; my preceptor had all the necessary moulds for making fireworks and we were skilled in the art of
making sky rockets and Roman candles for the Fourth of July celebra-
tion. These extra experiences did not demoralize the business nor the
apprentice; on the contrary they were personally useful and educational. Many changes have taken place since that period and I want to
refer to a few things . . . incidental to later times.

We [Lemberger and Co. in Lebanon, Pennsylvania] did sell
bear's grease and dog fat, while at the present time we are expected
to have polecat fat (or skunk fat), rabbit fat, opossum fat, goose
grease, rattle snake fat or oil, weasel skin, and eel skin because we
country druggists are supposed to have almost everything . . . It
was quite natural for an old lady . . . to write to us for [rattlesnake
skin for her rheumatism]. . . . We replied that we had none at
hand but it was possible for us to send her the article in a week or
ten days. . . . A person who hunted for rattlesnakes and who pre-

pared the skin and the oil for sale. . . . came into the store on the next day. . . . Next Saturday morning, when he left a package, imagine our surprise on opening it when we discovered a glass covered box with a three-foot rattler confined therein. . . . We wanted the skin without the snake. He enjoyed his joke, then took the snake home, killed and skinned it and prepared the fat.

G. G. C. Simms, District of Columbia, 1850s

The drug business, as conducted in the District of Columbia in the early fifties of the last century, was more professional than it is to-day [1906]. Many of the stores at that time did not handle soda water; and cigars were dealt in sparingly. To-day there is not a drug store in the city that has not a modern soda fountain, occupying the most prominent place, and next to it is a cigar case filled with the most popular brands of cigars. While paints and oils were dealt in to some extent in those days, they have now been discarded by nearly every pharmacist. The sale of confectionary by pharmacists is of recent introduction, and the business is important in most pharmacies. . . . Perfumery and toilet articles are dealt in more largely to-day, so are "patent" and "proprietary" medicines. The demand for the former is created by extensive advertising; physicians create the demand for the latter.

Very few elixirs were in use fifty years ago. Tablet triturates are of more recent origin. I think both of them are losing ground. Blister plasters have gone out of use. Rhubarb is little used, and calomel is used in very much smaller doses. Quinine is much more used now [1906] than it was in earlier years. More of it is used in the treatment of colds and grip than was used fifty years ago in the treatment of [malarial] chills and fever.

John M. Maisch (b. 1831-d.1893), Philadelphia, Pennsylvania, 1850-1856

When I arrived in America [1849] I had to battle with many difficulties until in Baltimore I met Dr. Wiss, a native of Nuremberg, who had lived in Berlin and has now returned there. He had the plan to open an apothecary, had me come to his house, gave me periodicals and books, most of which had more or less connection with pharmacy, but Soberheim [probably Johann F. Sobernheim] was for me the most important at that time. Through the druggist Vogeler I had the opportunity to become acquainted with drugs, and had charge of the apothecary until, in the summer of 1850, the [Wiss] store was opened, but by the end of 1851 had gone over into other hands. Then until the fall of 1853 I was employed in Washington, where I saw the American Journal of Pharmacy for the first time, took up the study of botany again, and was in such condition that I could acquire German journals and books.

After that I went to Philadelphia, because my father and one of my sisters had arrived there, and the following year the rest of the family came over. In the fall of '56 I worked for several months in a chemical factory on Furman Street, Brooklyn—I have forgotten the name—where strychnine, valeric acid and other chemicals were made, but the principal business was the adulteration of drugs. In 1856 I returned . . . to Philadelphia. Up to that time I had rarely had an opportunity to use a microscope, but toward the end of 1860 I induced the College to acquire one, and collected the necessary funds among the members. The instrument was diligently used, until I was able to have one of my own.

I became acquainted with Prof. [William] Procter in 1853, but with [Edward] Parrish not until 1856. To add anything more to the above would take me too much into detail, and I feel the sketch is sufficiently clear to show the beginning and my love for my pet subject.

Albert E. Magoffin (b. 1845), Bainbridge and Greenfield, Ohio, & Lyons, Kansas, 1856-1880s

One of my first duties in the drug life was the making of tinctures, syrups, etc. I can shut my eyes and look back to the later fifties and see a row of half-gallon and one-gallon specie jars sitting on a shelf in our back room [at father's drugstore], and I am reminded of the seven- and fourteen-day maceration periods, then straining through a cloth (no filter paper then that I recall). How I'd squeeze and squeeze those cloths to get out all liquid! We knew nothing of tincture presses. . . .

I recall the luscious Compound Cathartic Pill—that old-fashioned cure-all for everything but amputated legs. My stint was usually

2,000 [pills] every two months, sometimes oftener. How I hated that job. . . . No sugar-coating on ours; just plain pill, [bad] taste included. Along in 1871 or 1872 I bought a small sugar-coater, guaranteed to coat 200 pills at a time, but it was no good.

I remember that old powder called 'hicry picry' by our patrons [i.e., Hiera Picra]. I ground my own spices up till the eighties, and guaranteed them pure. I believe we had purer powdered drugs in those days than we have now [1906]; the get-rich schemers were not yet born. I wish I had a dollar for every ten-grain powder of calomel and every ten-grain pill of blue mass I have put up. Ten grains of either was not considered a big dose, but now the average dose of calomel is one-eighth or one-fourth of a grain. . . . Then [there's] that good old itch compound, Yclept Antguintem—the old name still sticks and is used by the older generation. Only a short time ago I had a call for it and did not dare to label it anything else; the real name would have made the man suspicious. Just at the close of the war [between the states] it had a wonderful sale. . . .

Prescription writing was not much in vogue when I first went into the business. A doctor would say [orally] how many pills to make, each to contain so many grains of this or that; or, so many ounces of syrup or mixture containing so many grains of such and such to a tea-spoonful. We would pencil it on a scrap of wrapping paper and go to work. . . . There was no refilling unless the doctor was present, and even he sometimes had to guess, as no copy was on file. . . .

Wonderful changes have taken place in the drug business in the fifty years I have been in it [and in the toiletries business]. The little square box containing . . . a pink ball for the complexion, and the little gaudy box of ten-cent face powder have given place to the numberless elegant toilet powders of today. The old-fashioned, long, transparent bar, one-inch square, of sassafrass-scented soap has given place to the highly perfumed soaps. The only tooth powder—orris root, powdered and mixed with finely powdered chalk—gives place to the tooth powders and liquid dentrifices. . . .

It is hard for us to realize that but a few years ago the druggist would either dig or buy roots and herbs to make many of his medicines. . . . Now proprietors ignore the importance of home-made products and buy largely [ready-made] articles that ought to be made at home. . . . Make your herbal tinctures from the leaves, roots or barks, instead of buying them or using fluidextracts. . . . If we did our own manufacturing now, as when I was young in the business, it would result in more real druggists and not so many machines.

Edward Parrish (b. 1822-d. 1872), Philadelphia, Pennsylvania, 1856

Much is said and written about the *science* and the *art* of Pharmacy, but in the present essay I propose to treat it as a *business*. . . .

If we apply to the pharmaceutical profession the question by which any pursuit is apt to be judged in this practical age and among business men, *How does it pay?* we shall have to admit that it compares unfavorably either with most kinds of mercantile business or with the so-called learned professions.

It resembles a trade in some respects and a profession in others. Considered as a trade, it is limited in the extent and nature of its wares. . . . [and is] almost of necessity a comparatively small business.

Allied to the professions, Pharmacy is considered as occupying a subordinate position. The apothecary, although equal to the physician in the responsibility incurred, is inferior in the range of knowledge required and in the compensation awarded. His knowledge, skill and integrity, however, constitute the larger part of his capital, and these . . . are too much overlooked by his customers. . . .

It will be obvious, at a glance, that the increase of articles of commerce [aromatics, essential oils, confectionary, chemicals, spirituous liquors, and surgical and obstetrical instruments], so far as a market for them exists, is a certain means of increased revenue. The variety called for by the wants of the public . . . is sufficient to furnish considerable scope for the investment of capital and the judicious direction of energy and enterprise.

But the business of the apothecary has an important relation to manufacturing, and it is in this that its principal profit exists. Our largest profits are on articles of our own preparation. . . . The apothecary, who is alive to his own interests, should not fail to prepare every kind of medicine for which there is a demand.

As far as the Pharmacopoeia goes it will be his guide; beyond that, he must rely upon known or approved formulas or publish his own. . . . Let him issue his remedies, appropriately labelled with a plain statement of their composition, uses and adaptations, so that physicians may prescribe them by their names, and the public, becoming acquainted with their merits, may avail themselves of them without medical advice. Let me not here be understood as countenancing quackery; the course now recommended tends directly toward the most practicable method ridding ourselves and the public of this terrible scourge. . . . The apothecary should never, on his labels or in his advertisements, stoop to evasions and subterfuges. . . . Nothing so establishes a man in the favor of the community as inflexible honesty. . . .

I may advert to other profitable opening[s] in the line of pharmaceutical manufacture, namely, the improvement of the quality of pharmaceutical preparations, and the multiplication of new remedies. A pharmaceutist can hardly fail to improve his business by fostering among physicians who resort to his shop a taste for the finer products of the pharmaceutical art; these command a higher price than the old and more familiar remedies, and whether really better for the purpose designed or not, they gratify a taste for novelty and for elegance which we can ill afford to disregard. . . .

The profits of retailing medicines have diminished by the increased cost to the retailer of the raw materials and of the principal solvent he employs, while the tendency under the spirit of competition, without the restraints of a just and wise conservatism, is to lower the prices charged, and to bring the business down to a level of a trade, and a poor one at the best. . . .

If we would see our profession rising in social standing and influence, we must cease to compete in prices, join in holding up the standard of remuneration to a just and reasonable point, and by a liberal and fraternal policy toward each other, and a dignified bearing toward the public, show that our profession merits a higher consideration than pertains to a mere trader, and that the pharmaceutist deserves to be remunerated for his knowledge and skill as well as for the wares he offers for sale.

Frederick W. Fenn, Delaware, 1857

There were no regular pharmacies [in the state] outside of Wilmington in 1857 except in a few instances. In the small villages the general store kept a line of domestic remedies, while prescriptions and physicians' supplies were obtained in the [larger] towns. The town drug stores were usually combined with hardware, and additional sidelines were stationery and books, wall paper, paints, and oils. Some druggists sent out wagons filled with all sorts of domestic medicines to supply country general stores.

S. A. D. Sheppard (b. 1842-d. 1915), Salem, Massachusetts, 1858-1868

The store at Salem, Mass., in which I spent ten years as boy and clerk, 1858 to 1868, was established in the early years of the nineteenth century and it is still [in 1906] the leading drug store of that city. When I went there as a boy the senior partner, Dr. Benjamin F. Browne, was very active, and our store was one of the centers for the discussion of Salem's general and public interests. . . . He had no use for vacation, never having missed a day at the store for more than forty years. He had his own formulas for all the old-time preparations—paregoric, tincture of rhubarb, 'elixir pro,' [probably Elixir Proprietatis, i.e., Tinctura Aloes et Myrrhae], Stoughton's bitters, stramonium ointment, etc., all of which we made in large quantities, supplying the small dealers within ten miles around. . . .

[George F. H.] Markoe and I were boys together in the grammar school at Salem, but he did not go to the high school, so went into the drug business. . . . He idolized William Procter, Jr., and read everything that Procter wrote that he could get hold of. I well remember how he worked over cream syrups for the soda fountain when Procter sent out some formulas. . . . His enthusiasm was what really made our [local association, the Massachusetts] College a teaching institution and he did the work [as instructor] under most discouraging circumstances. . . .

Part II:
1860-1933

INTRODUCTION

As the U.S. Civil War unfolded, the specter of untold numbers of wounded (nearly 300,000 eventually on the Union side alone) implied a sudden and insatiable need for pharmaceutical supplies. One byproduct of this wartime experience was a technologic and financial foundation for the industrialization of drug-making for the nation at large. That meant fundamental change in the role of the "corner druggist"—a wrenching and uncontrollable change—of which echoes can be heard in the reminiscences of *Drugstore Memories.*

Firms like E. R. Squibb had grown rapidly to meet the military orders for ether and compounding ingredients. At war's end, the industry turned its increased capacity to the civilian manufacture of medicinals, many of which had been traditionally produced in-shop. The manufacturing aspect of pharmacy practice—an important distinction between the apothecary and ordinary merchants—disappeared during the decades following the war. A modern industry arose that became a force in day-to-day pharmacy practice.

The Civil War also brought about a cease-fire in the turf battle between pharmacists and physicians. After the war, however, the truce quickly ended. Many physicians went back to dispensing and many pharmacists still prescribed from behind the counter. Moreover, physicians and the press began calling for the regulation of poison sales and pharmacy practice in general. Organized pharmacy, working with a model pharmacy law written by John Maisch, eventually cooperated in this effort, which led to mandatory requirements for licensure as a pharmacist and to the regulation of pharmacy practice via state laws passed in the 1870s, 80s, and 90s.

Physicians had pushed hard for pharmacy regulation, arguing that incompetence was rife. They had a point: As large firms increasingly took over the basic manufacturing of pharmaceuticals, the expertise of pharmacists narrowed. It took considerable skill to make a good quality fluidextract from a crude plant. It took no particular skill to buy that fluidextract from Squibb or Lilly and was usually less costly in time and money.

With manufacture disappearing, many pharmacists moved their prescription departments to the back of the store. Here the filling of prescriptions was done behind a screen. These changes were part of a trend, which also involved other types of retailers who had featured inhouse fabrication of goods.

This remodeling opened up the front of shops for more elaborate soda fountains. Pharmacists had the chemical knowledge to operate the cranky carbonated water generators and had the pharmaceutical skills to make fresh flavorings and mix complicated confections. Along with the soda fountain, a particular mixture of goods—including tobacco, candy, magazines, soaps, flavorings, and patent medicines—came to be seen as the "sundries" that characterized one of America's distinctive institutions, the drugstore.

From the late 19th century up through the 1940s, the mainstay of the American drugstore was the "out front" merchandise. A combination of factors—physician dispensing, the small number of effective drugs, and destructive competition among a surplus of pharmacies—kept the prescription practice from being more than a small fraction of the average store owner's income. Yet, it was this special combination of the commercial and the professional that gave a special character to the life behind drugstore counters that practitioners recall on the following pages.

The march of technology during the late 19th and early 20th centuries heavily impacted pharmacy. Improved communications and transportation improved drug supply. New drugs began to appear from chemical laboratories (e.g., antipyretics and hypnotics) and more popular dosage forms (e.g., capsules and compressed tablets) supplanted older, less palatable forms. Throughout the period, however, the old problems lingered—physician dispensing, price cutting, and patent-medicine quackery—while new ones arose. Drugstore chains had existed in the late nineteenth century but took off in the young twentieth. In 1909 Charles Walgreen opened his second store and by 1927 had acquired 116. The giant in this field, Louis K. Liggett, amassed a chain of nearly 700 drug-stores between 1907 and 1930. Department stores opened pharmacies as well. Mass marketers and discounters cut prices on many items that had been stable for decades. The young National Association of Retail Druggists (f. 1898) fought unsuccessfully for plans to sustain prices. Aggressive competition struck hard, causing a contraction in the number of drugstores relative to population.

Higher standards of education for pharmacists gradually improved their role in health care. The first pharmacy curriculum at a state university was offered in 1868 at the University of Michigan. Others soon followed at Wisconsin, Purdue, Iowa, Ohio State, and Kansas. Pharmacy education began its long climb from technical training to full academic status. In 1905 New York State passed a bellwether law requiring graduation from a pharmacy school course (2-year minimum) before licensure, which was soon emulated nationally. In 1928, the American Association of Colleges of Pharmacy adopted a four-year bachelor's degree as the requirement for all schools in good standing. By the early 1930s, pharmacy had laid the groundwork for full professional status, but the commercialized nature of day-to-day practice prevented this from occurring until after World War II. Only then did efforts toward educational reform, energized by the Pharmaceutical Survey of 1946-49, lead to a research-based profession.

Historians refer to the first two decades of the twentieth century as the Progressive Era for the efforts of Theodore Roosevelt, William Taft, and Woodrow Wilson to rein in the excesses of capitalism. This approach included the pioneering social legislation represented by the Food and Drugs Act in 1906 and the Harrison Narcotic Act in 1914. The Progressive movement ended in 1919 as the nation suffered under high inflation and disillusionment over the League of Nations and other postwar disappointments.

With the onset of national Prohibition (1920-1933), drugstore soda fountains replaced taverns as social gathering places. By 1929, roughly 60 percent of American drugstores had fountains. Sales of out-front merchandise improved as well. The majority of Americans now lived in cities and towns, and drugstores expanded their product lines to meet demand. With the advent of Prohibition, one demand arose from an epidemic of prescriptions for "medicinal" alcohol. While the physiologic effects of alcohol had given it some role in therapeutics for centuries, this new kind of American epidemic eventually made pharmacists and physicians the target of both regulators and humorists.

The Great Depression of the 1930s hit pharmacy hard but not as severely as some retail trades. Most pharmacists augmented their income by selling a variety of inexpensive necessities, such as toiletries, household chemicals, soaps, flavorings, and tobacco products. The soda-fountain delights continued to attract the populace to American drugstores during the 1930s. But during World War II the labor shortages made this major sideline more problem than benefit for many pharmacy owners. Coupled with the advantage to be gained by finding more profitable use for the space, this meant that fountains gradually disappeared in the ensuing years. Predatory price cutting among purveyors of drugstore products made survival problematic for many owners, although state laws on "fair trade" began, during the 1930s, to bring some relief.

In the early decades of the twentieth century, pharmacy practice was evolving. Physician dispensing continued to decline and physician's prescriptions became simpler. The "shotgun" recipes of previous generations (e.g., 3 to 5 active ingredients in a vehicle) were being replaced by single-entity dosage forms. Prescribing increased after effective synthetic drugs such as aspirin and arsphenamine emerged from laboratories in Europe. By the 1930s, about a third of prescriptions called for brand-named products. Still, the vast majority of medicines sold in drugstores throughout the period were either "druggists' preparations," i.e., standard remedies bearing the pharmacist's own store label, or were nostrums. Only after World War II did an influx of new drugs and greater access to healthcare make the prescription department the financial "engine" of the average American pharmacy.

The reminiscences in Part 2 reflect some of the frustrations connected with the odd position of the pharmacist between the Civil War and World War II. Pharmacists managed a general emporium of inexpensive goods and only occasionally filled prescription orders (6 to 12 times a day on average). Yet the professional aspect of the American drugstore was essential to its special niche in the community.

As one reads the tales from behind the counter, it may be tempting to be nostalgic for a time when pharmacists could have a leisurely visit with "customers" rather than urgently counsel "patients." The "corner druggist" was a fixture of American life and as a small businessman he believed enthusiastically in the American dream of success. Along his journey, the world within his shop was full of adventures, as the following pages attest.

REMINISCENCES

W. P. Carstarphen, Hannibal, Missouri, 1860-1864

I moved to Hannibal, Missouri [from New London], where I entered [the drug] business on my own account. I was there when the [Civil] War broke out, and during the whole four years that it lasted. You must remember that our portion of the State was a battle ground between the North and South, where a sort of guerrilla warfare was waged incessantly. . . .

In those days we paid, on the Mississippi river, $3.50 to $4 an ounce for quinine. P. & W. [Powers & Weightman] in ounce bottles was the only kind sold. Capsules were at that time unknown. The most popular mode of administering quinine was about ten grains dissolved in two ounces of Spiritus Frumenti, repeated every two or three hours. . . . We sold it at ten cents a drink, i.e., when mixed with quinine. . . . The Poor Man's Plaster [a mixture of beeswax, tar and resin] was the only plaster I remember as being kept ready-spread. The rest were spread on [sheep or kid] skin as they were needed, either on prescription or called for by the public. All ointments were made [in the pharmacy], and many hard hours' work I put in making mercurial ointment.

Tinctures were the principal liquid medicine; later, fluid extracts were introduced. . . . Tinctures sold from ten to twenty cents per ounce during the war. Alcohol was worth $5 to $6.50 per gallon, and oftentimes hard to get [even] at that price. Turpentine, being distilled entirely in the South, became extremely hard to get, and consequently very high in price . . . as high as $1 per pint. We used naptha in its stead for mixing paints, etc.

Our prices on prescriptions rated ten to fifteen cents per ounce; pills, except quinine, fifteen cents per dozen; plasters that we spread were usually 4x6" and sold for twenty-five cents. In early times we

71

never got out prescription blanks [to the doctors]. A doctor would just use an old envelope, a paper sack, or a piece of letter paper. Blanks were introduced after the war, and we fell in line.

Hannibal in those days was a city of 12,000; and a store on a prominent corner—say about 22x50 feet—would rent for from $40 to $50 per month. . . . I remember one day a band of uniformed militia, composed principally of the roughest element, entered the town, helped themselves to what whiskey could be found, shouting and singing 'John Brown's Body' etc. They procured a barber's pole from a shop near by, and with the end smashed in all our [drugstore] windows. . . . Some forty or fifty came into the store, and I began to think life behind a drug counter was not what it was pictured. . . . The Federal troops often came into the store with a list of what they wanted and we would put it up, but never got any pay for the drugs that we furnished to either side.

J. H. Zielin, Charleston (?), South Carolina, c. 1860-1865

As soon as the election of Mr. Lincoln was confirmed the trade was thrown into confusion in regard to credit and finance. . . . Prices of drugs were rapidly advancing and, as most of our goods were bought in the North, the condition of the country deterred many from purchasing for fear of not being able to pay or to get the drugs through the blockade when purchased. The question of obtaining a drug supply became a serious one. . . . First the lighter drugs were smuggled through by refugees. . . . The smuggling was confined to the frontier, at first through Maryland and Virginia, then through Kentucky, the West, etc., and finally—as hostilities continued—the only means of obtaining supplies to any extent was by blockade runners to Savannah, Charleston, New Orleans and Mobile. By degrees stocks became much broken, and many—finding the leading articles exhausted—sold out their stores.

Some [druggists] believed in selling their stock at the prices then thought high; others believed in buying all they could regardless of price. . . . Persons who hesitated to buy sal-soda at $100 a pound afterward boldly bought it at $600. Opium at $100 per ounce seemed cheap a year after, when it brought $2,000 per pound. Brandy sold for $150 per pint, and everything else was proportionately high. . . .

Considering the liability and inducements to adulterate, it was not so common as may have been expected. Strange as it may seem the medicine brought in by the blockade runners was of the best. . . . The [Confederate] Government generally took first choice of what was needed and the balance of the cargo would be advertised and sold at auction at the port of entry. On the day of sale it was interesting to note the arrival of druggists from all parts of the Confederacy. . . .

After Mr. Lincoln's proclamation declaring medicines contraband of war, indignation was very great, and to counteract this the Conscript Act exempted druggists in the proportion of one to each establishment. . . . In certain districts druggists were appointed by the State authorites to supply medicine, and details [i.e., assignments] for medical purposes would be also secured from the army. To be a druggist, therefore, was to be a privileged and envied person. Efforts were made especially to keep up the supply of adhesive plasters . . . So highly was this plaster estimated that in Sherman's march to the sea the field surgeon had orders issued to have this plaster preserved whenever captured with stores. . . .

The straits to which druggists were driven were many. Tupelo-wood was used for corks, and rough glass bottles were made in Richmond. The earth of a smoke-house [used to cure meat] was percolated for salt and saltpeter; and soon cold water was the only remedy for healing wounds.

Before planting it was a universal custom in the South to soak seed-wheat in a solution of bluestone [copper sulfate] to prevent rust. The wartime scarcity of bluestone soon advanced its price to $25 per pound in trade, which was the only way it could be bought. It was quite the custom to exchange with the farmer one pound of bluestone for one bushel of wheat. With this wheat in hand the druggist could purchase anything that could be had, so that it may literally be said the druggist lived on bluestone.

Farmers got alarmed as to the value of money and would not sell provisions for Confederate scrip. If you had nothing to barter, provisions were difficult to secure. The taking of the one-tenth of everything by the government as tithes made the farmer avoid marketing provisions. This often reduced the citizen to the edge of despair and some times starvation looked the best people in the face. The government was also reduced to great straits to feed the army as well as pris-

*Military pharmacy during the Civil War—Union and Confederate—was largely
in the hands of "hospital stewards," shown here dispensing from a medical supply
wagon at a field hospital of the Union Army. The Civil War affected the practice
of pharmacy variously (for example, C. B. Johnson, below, and J. H. Zielin, p.
72). (Engraving from* Harper's Weekly, *11 March 1865, 149.)*

oners. This taking of tithes was necessitated, and if the farmers did not
come to town the plantations were visited, and the tithes demanded.

At times requisition would be made on the druggist's stock, and
many articles were taken from dire necessity, although as a general
thing they were respected in their rights. Guards were stationed at the
corners of the streets in cities to demand your papers and an explana-
tion why you were not at the front. Woe to him who had lost or mis-
laid his druggist exemption papers.

Charles Beneulyn Johnson (b.1843),
Memphis, Tennessee and Vicksburg, Mississippi, 1863-1864

About the middle of January, 1863, a comrade of mine, a warm
friend, was taken seriously sick and had to be removed to our regimen-

tal hospital. That he might have special care and be made as comfortable as possible, I accompanied him thither and remained with him some weeks till his friends came from the North and took him home to die. Becoming acquainted with the surgeons in charge and liking them, and not caring for the irregular and mixed duties of a soldier left about the city [of Memphis], I was induced to remain and become a regular hospital attaché. . . .

Our first Hospital Steward was James M. Miller, of Greenville, Ill., where he had served an apprenticeship in his father's drug store, and where he now resides [1917] and has the reputation of being the wealthiest man in his county. As Ward Master of the Regimental Hospital I served a sort of apprenticeship under Hospital Steward Miller, and later, when he saw fit to become a commissioned officer in a colored regiment, I succeeded to his position. This was not because I was as well qualified for the place as I should have been, but because I was the best fitted for it of anyone who was available. I had had a little Latin, a little chemistry, a little physics, a little higher mathematics before joining the army, and very shortly after I entered I began familiarizing myself with drugs and chemicals, and with such other duties as might fall to the lot of a hospital attaché. Indeed, I studied so hard that sometimes things became confused in my mind. A condition not always any too safe to work under. . . .

One peculiar method of prescribing was in vogue. . . . A number of favorite prescriptions for sundry diseases were put up in quantity and each given a number; consequently, instead of having to write out a prescription and having it put up separately, the surgeon had but to designate a number, and in short order the patient would have the desired remedy.

We had a few medical books, among which I recall "Pereira's Materia Medica," "Mendenhall's Vade Mecum," a work on chemistry; "Parrish's Pharmacy," and "Gray's Anatomy."

During a campaign our stock of medicines was necessarily limited to standard remedies, among which could be named opium, morphine, Dover's powder, quinine, rhubarb, Rochelle salts, Epsom salts, castor oil, sugar of lead, tannin, sulphate of copper, sulphate of zinc, camphor, tincture of opium, tincture of iron, tinctura opii camphorata, syrup of squills, simple syrup, alcohol, whiskey, brandy, port wine, sherry wine, etc. Upon going into camp, where we were likely to remain a few days, these articles were unpacked and put on temporary shelves made from boxlids; and, on the other hand, when marching orders came, the medicines were again packed in boxes, the bottles protected from breaking by old papers, etc.

Practically all the medicines were administered in powder form or in the liquid state. Tablets had not yet come into use, and pills were very far from being as plentiful as they are today. The result was that most powders were stirred in water and swallowed. In the case of such medicine as quinine, Dover's powder, tannin, etc., the dose thus prepared was a bitter one. The bromides, sulfonal, trional and similar soporifics and sedatives were about all the Civil War surgeon had to relieve nervousness and induce sleep.

(Copyright 1917, by F. A. Davis Co.)

H. M. Parchen, Montana, 1860s

In the summer of 1864 gold was discovered in Last Chance Gulch, and the present city of Helena sprang up. R. S. Hale opened the first drug store there; the writer followed in March 1865 and is [now, 1906] the oldest druggist in business in Montana.

My firm started with groceries and drugs, and continued the two lines until 1869, when the grocery department was closed. With a capital of $3,500 we sold $99,600 worth of goods the first fifteen months we were in business, and made a profit of over $18,000.

During three months of the year goods came by way of the Missouri River to Fort Benton, the head of navigation, 140 miles from Helena. After winter closed navigation, goods had to come 1,500 miles overland at a cost at times of 30 cents a pound. This brought very high prices for indispensable articles, which then were bought up by speculators, who advanced the prices further. We paid, for example, $6 per dozen for 25-cent preparations and $24 per dozen for $1 preparations, and retailed them at $1 for 25-cent articles and $3 for the $1 articles. . . . In the fall of 1867, when we received a shipment from San Francisco . . . it came via ocean to Portland, thence up the Columbia River to the head of navigation, and thence (at 40 cents per pound) by pack train.

In those days the prescription trade was small, most people resorting to nostrums or the compounds made by druggists. No prescription was filled for less than $1. There were few physicians and these were mostly of the old school and from the South, who had "read" medicine in some country town.

John W. Ballard, Davenport, Iowa, 1860s

Pharmacy in eastern Iowa (Davenport) in the early sixties had somewhat of a department store character; and some departments could hardly be classed as "elegant pharmacy." For instance, many heavy drugs were handled and, with these, tar, pitch, rosin, paint, and lubricating oils—nor were these put up in convenient packages. A customer would call for tar in quantities from "a nickel's worth" to a gallon or more, and these varied demands were all supplied from a barrel. Especially in the winter season, this was not a delicate task.

"Patent" medicines were fewer in number than now [1906], while proprietary remedies for physicians' use were unknown, except Norwood's tincture and McMunn's elixir. Physicians, almost without exception, wrote prescriptions [rather than dispense from their offices]. As [mass produced] tablets and sugar-coated pills were unknown, they devised formulas for each individual patient, and these in most cases called for remedies made by the pharmacist, so that much time was required in the laboratory. . . .

Transportation facilities were not as good then, the water route being used much more; our bottles were shipped down the Ohio River from Pittsburg and up the Mississippi. Shipments of heavy drugs from New York were made by canal, and then by steam around the lake, requiring six weeks in transit.

Drugs required in powder form we mostly reduced by hand, and plasters were made to order and spread on sheepskin. All pills likewise were made when ordered, and none were kept in stock except Compound Cathartic and Compound Rhubarb. It was a life of labor to be a pharmacist, and yet we always think of "the good old days."

Fred R. Dimmitt (b. c.1845?), Missouri, 1860s

In 1863 my brother and I went into the drug business at Seventh and Olive streets, St. Louis (population about 150,000). In 1865 my brother and I began manufacturing a proprietary article. Two years later we fitted up a fancy wagon drawn by two fine mules, which I drive all over Missouri, selling this preparation and druggists' goods, and in that way visited almost every druggist in the State. The only railroads in Missouri at that time were the Old Hannibal & St. Joe, the North Missouri, the Missouri-Pacific (completed as far as Kansas City), and the Frisco, running only to Rolla.

In my travels, especially in Southwest Missouri, I at times would drive all day and see nothing but chimnies standing where formerly stood happy homes. These homes had been destroyed by either the federal or confederate armies.

John Best, Central City, Colorado, 1866-1870s

I graduated from the New York College of Pharmacy in 1865, and like many other young men of that time "went West," settling down in Central City, Colorado, in 1866, and opening a drug store there. Central City at that time was the largest city in Colorado, deriving its population and prosperity from the rich mining region of which it was the center. Our city boasted of six drug stores, all prosperous and friendly, and all conducted by educated pharmacists. . . . Most of our trade was professional, there being comparatively few patent medicines sold. Such as we carried [were] sold at an average of 50 percent over the regular prices in the East. Hostetter's Bitters, Ayer's, Hood's, Schenck's and other proprietary remedies were in good demand, Ayer's especially.

Strange to say, perfumery was very popular, and I sold vast quantities of Lubin's extracts and soaps (the favorite brand) at one dollar per bottle or cake. Hair oil was another great favorite, and we reaped an honest profit by dispensing lard oil perfumed with bergamot, under the popular name of "Bear's Oil," at 25 cents an ounce. Much of my business, as with other druggists, was the supplying of chemicals used in the mining industry, quicksilver being one of the principal items. Most of these chemicals were obtained from St. Louis, that being the headquarters for overland shipping. . . .

Druggists were compelled to buy or order staple drugs and chemicals in large quantities because of the length of time required for shipment and the high freight charges. . . . I would order a quantity of each article sufficient to last for six months or a year, for when the

The steam ship and steam train brought striking changes to the procurement and distribution of natural drug products from around the world. (Engravings from the Bi-monthly Prices Current, *January 1876, of drug-importer W. H. Schieffelin & Co.)*

stock was sold out it was out, generally for some months. We Colorado druggists also had to be very careful in timing our orders to prevent damage to goods by climatic changes in transit. Thus, every preparation that would freeze at low temperatures had to be ordered so that it would be in transit over the plains and mountains during the summer season, this often requiring three or four months. It was customary to send in our principal orders twice a year, so that shipments could be made at the most advantageous time. . . . The "fast freight" had mules for motive power, the average time between Colorado and eastern cities being three months, at a cost of 22 cents a pound. "Ordinary freight" shipments and heavy drugs and chemicals came to us by ox teams, and six months was the usual time, . . . at 10 cents a pound. . . . Often several druggists would combine their orders so as to secure original bulk packages and thus cheaper freight charges. We made most of our galenicals, it being cheaper to buy the crude drugs and alcohol, and make them, than to pay freight on finished products. Another factor was the cost of packages. Everything shipped by the freight wagons had to be as compact as possible and in containers not liable to breakage. . . .

Business was mostly on a cash basis. The only barter was with the Indians of nearby villages who offered furs, etc. in trade for their wants. . . . Except for the necessary crudities of a new country and our isolation by distance from pharmaceutical manufacturing centers, the drug business was pretty much the same as is still found [1913] in small country villages. [But] we had our share of Indian warfare when the Utes went on the warpath in 1866 to 1867, and Colorado was practically cut off from all communication with the eastern states for months.

John Uri Lloyd (b.1849-d.1936), Cincinnati, Ohio, 1860s

I was "bound" for two years to an apprenticeship to "learn pharmacy," beginning, as my preceptor expressed it, "at the bottom," which I soon found to mean, literally, at the bottom. My day was to begin at seven o'clock in the morning, when I was to be at the Post Office to get the mail and take it to the store. Every morning I was to sweep the store, clean up the soda counter, wash all the glasses, wash the bottles for the prescription counter and case, clean the graduates and mortars used in compounding prescriptions, once a week wash all the windows, run errands as necessity required, fill the soda syrups and wait on the soda counter, and at odd times, put in my time filling and folding Seidlitz Powders. For performing these duties, I was to receive $2.00 a week the first six months, $2.50 the next six months, $3.00 the third six months, and $4.00 the remaining six months.

Of the several boys in that establishment, I was the only one thus apprenticed. The others were simply employed, and received much higher pay than came to me, their object being only the usual returns that come from business. . . .

With Mr. [George] Eger, I was especially to be taught prescription pharmacy. He taught me not only the natures of the different drugs, but their doses and actions. He himself was extremely particular in this direction, and never did he fill a prescription till he was sure that the dosage was correct. In case he was not sure, he looked it up in the authorities then used, and I once saw him spend an entire hour hunting up the dosage of some obscure substance. After I myself began filling prescriptions under his care, he enforced upon me the same rule; and I was required not only to know the dosage of each remedy mentioned in a prescription but the amount that would be an over-dose. It was then the custom among German physicians, when writing a prescription that carried a substance in what was under ordinary circumstances an overdose, to place above the prescription the "square root" sign, thus certifying that the prescription stood as it was meant to be. . . .

Well do I remember when atropine was introduced for dilating the pupil of the eye. It came to us in the form of the alkaloid itself, and the pharmacist made it soluble with the exact amount of dilute sulphuric acid required, a very delicate process. The favorite prescription of physicians (this was before the day of professional oculists) was one-half grain of atropine, water one ounce, sulphuric acid q.s., to make a solution. Bear in mind that this was for use in the eye.

John T. Moore (b. c.1845-d.1932), Kansas, c.1860-1880.

[In the West] the getting of stock to manufacture and sell was . . . difficult. Stores were usually a long way from the source of supplies; . . . everything had to come from places east of the Mississippi. . . . When drugs were bought it was directly advantageous to buy a lasting quantity of non-perishable things if transportation conditions were favorable. . . . The druggist timed a spring or autumn purchasing period. . . . The arrival of . . . aggregations of stock was anticipated keenly by the younger rustling workers of the drug emporium, who were sometimes at a loss to know where they would house it when it came.

Crude drugs were received in bulk paper packages—it was before the day of the ready-made paper bags. . . . The making of a package by a supplying wholesaler in those days was a fine art. The completed unit from an Eastern supplier was often a bit of handsome mass shaping, with the sides level and the ends and corners square. The irregularities of a three or four-pound package of lump benzoin were made to subside into a more or less quadrilateral mass by jolting and suasion and patting and squeezing in a rather large sheet of browny white paper.

A ten-pound package of senna leaves . . . was more easily packed, but reminded me of the filling of a cushion tick with goose feathers. It took strong string and a tricky application of pressure to shape that bundle. If anyone wishes to experience the necessary skill involved in the art of making a presentable retail package in the days when paper sacks were not, let him try to wrap up half a pound of whole flax seed for "cough tea" in a flat sheet of paper making a tight rectangular package of it.

As a note, by the way, it may be set down that the little labor-saving paper sack tended to benumb the skill in pharmaceutical neat-package dispensing. A two- or three-ounce package of flowers of sulphur or four ounces of bicarbonate of soda used to be rapidly furnished at the common sale counter in neat, tapering, flat-sided, oblong packages with wedge-shaped ends, which showed care, suggested safety, and invited confidence. . . . A decade or so after the paper sack had come into use . . . its inroads in supplanting drug daintiness was marked. The newer drug clerk would throw a few sticks of kitchen cinnamon higgedly-piggedly into a much too large ready-made sack, scribble a pencilled something on the delivery item, and let it go at that, with too many fluttering twine endings that emphasize its awkwardness. In the years before, the clerk would assemble the scrolls of bark in fairly equal lengths on a sheet of white drug paper and shape them into an acceptable package without protruding pieces—he would then have applied a sticking label, ink-written and legible. . . .

With every drug store owner necessarily a manufacturer, the quantity of a preparation made up in the back room was dictated by experience learned of his trade necessities. . . . It was a rarity to find a laboratory with any large utensil not in use. . . .

Customers' wants and demands were entirely different from what the modern [ca.1930] pharmacist would vision to be possible; so the home manufacturing and multivarious all-day compounding were enforced activities. The simplest needs of a customer were seldom "hand outs"; what he demanded called for some work, involving measuring, weighing, mortar-and-pestle mixing, milling, sieving to all degrees of coarseness and fineness—the sieves of brass, iron or bolting cloth, the latter perhaps begged of the local flour miller—the using of varied applications and intensities of heat; all these were normal functions of the practice of pharmacy. . . .

Perhaps a dozen of so-called patent medicines [were available] as nostrums for prevailing ailments. . . . In the Eastern states there were probably a greater variety of such offerings, . . . most . . . made for local sale in well-populated centers and came not West. . . . In those days when a gallon of whiskey could be bought for "a quarter," the bottle of stuff purporting to be a tonic had to be ostentatiously liberal in size to tempt the dollars of the imaginary sick people. . . . Even in the new West a form of proprietary medicine was nevertheless region-ally popular in the sense that many of the stores in the larger commu-nities put up ready-to-dispense sizes of medicines for prevailing sick-nesses. . . .

It was rare for a new settler to come to the West without his reci-pes (or as he called it "receipt" book) of emergency things. . . . These recipe books offered a solution for every trouble. . . . It was hard to find a drug store without a "file" of these volumes of cyclopaedic knowledge. The pages devoted to dyeing were hard worked and bore visible evidence of it. There were no dyes of manufactured organic chemical origin—no packaged dyes. . . . The drug man who could im-part the most practical instructions was the idol of the farmer's wife.

William H. Rogers, New York, 1861-1880s

"Druggists" we called ourselves; "pharmaceutist" was the nearest we got to the later "pharmacist." Pharmacy laws were unknown in the days of which I speak [the 1860s]. Anyone who chose could sell drugs, yet the business was practically given up to the druggist by general consent. . . . In the fifties, physicians' prescriptions were few; their number gained rapidly in the sixties, reached its zenith in the seventies and eighties, and then in the early nineties the "horrors" of the [mass-produced] tablet and the "manufacturer's specialty" began to loom ominously upon the horizon.

All physicians bought their supplies of the druggists—doctors in remote country districts buying crude drugs, powders and tinctures in quantity. If we had few prescriptions we made up for it in the many domestic recipes for families and for farm stock. A larger proportion of the sales than now [1906] were recipes for medicines, and a larger pro-portion called for technical knowledge than now. Synthetic products were unknown. . . . Ready-made pills were unknown. . . . Few fluid extracts were used. Tinctures in the fifties were largely made by mac-eration, percolation being a rarity. My experience began in 1861, which seemed the awakening of a new era [in pharmacy]. Evidence of the old era was all about me: the drug mill, the mortar and pestle, and the pill tile, which were in use hourly.

Many crude dyewoods and dyestuffs were sold, largely indigo in some areas. Annato [a yellow coloring for butter and cheese] was sold by the ounce for family use and in 50-pound baskets to creameries. Who sells annatto these days? Or cochineal? Or madder? . . . The first prepared dyes that came to my notice was in the early sixties: Howe & Stevens family dyes, composed of dyewoods with blue vitriol and other mordants, all in one. Analin in all its vivid hues burst upon the world a few years later, and the older forms of dyes died quickly.

"Patent" medicines were fewer in number—the leading ones "on consignment". . . . Less soothing syrup, Godfrey's cordial, paregoric and other children's narcotics are sold now [1906] than then, also less opium, morphine, and laudanum for adults—a great improvement. The younger generation of doctors is more careful in ordering such things. The variety of drugs demanded was but a fraction of those now needed. . . . There was less dead stock, especially of drugs and chemicals bought at exaggerated prices and of ephemeral popularity.

We sold most of the toilet goods bought by the community. Old-fashioned cologne was largely used, and hair oil, as were "genuine" ox-marrow pomade and "bear's oil." All country drug stores sold paints, oils and window glass. Many yet do so in this section [of New York state]. . . . Families used "burning fluid" as an illuminant, composed of three parts of alcohol and one part of purified oil of turpentine. It was highly inflammable but competed with whale and sperm oils as illuminants—all of which druggists sold. This was before the war [between the states] and alcohol was worth less than 50 cents per gallon. Stores were lighted with "camphine"—a purified oil of turpentine, burned with a round wick, brilliant and dangerous.

Profits were much larger, largely because the crude drugs or chemicals were converted into pills, tinctures, syrups, emulsions or ointments by the druggist, with correspondingly greater pay [as return] for labor and skill. Special brands were never exploited or prescribed in the good old days [before the ?1870s]. . . .

As to the quality of drugs, there was more adulteration then than now [1906], greater need for close scrutiny. . . . The United States Dispensatory, Parrish's Pharmacy, Fownes' Chemistry, Gray's Botany—these and a few other standard works, when mastered, formed a solid foundation. . . . More fortunate youths of to-day are taken by the hand and led through our excellent colleges of pharmacy. In the rush and bustle of modern business conditions, few could otherwise attain proficiency. . . . The modern drug establishment must possess the technical skill, but the larger proportion of the business is purely commercial and that commercial portion must be of high order of skill and merit if the drug store is to survive, as by pharmacy alone not one store in a score could live.

Charles H. Zahn (b. c.1851), St. Louis, Missouri, 1860s-1890s

Being an apprentice, I had to have a permit and my father had to sign for me, for four years. My salary was $10.00 a month for the first year, $12.00 a month for the second year, $12.50 for the third year, and $16.00 for the fourth year.

. . . Roots had to be cut, which was a job for an apprentice. I remember the Galanga, the toughest root of them all. I had to tie a wet handkerchief over my mouth and nose to keep from inhaling the dust, as I cut and ground. Ginseng root came from Kentucky, and the closer these roots represented a human figure the higher was the price.

And I made my own plasters. Poor Man's plaster, adhesive plasters, Cantharides plaster to fit behind the ear for eye diseases, and Mother's plaster for boils were among those I made. All sold for five cents apiece. I sold many essential oils, such as anise, cinnamon, etc. I worked in the laboratory by day and studied at night under one gas jet. I read not only in English but also read the Prussian Pharmacopoea, since the trade was then around 90% German. . . . I had learned both German and English at school in Cincinnati, and spoke German in my home and in the stores.

It was in 1872 that I arrived in the struggling frontier town of St. Louis. My first job was with a Mrs. Mack, who operated a drug store [opened by her late husband] on Carondelet and Lafayette Avenues. [After experience in several other drugstores] I took charge of the drug store in the Barnum Hotel, under the name of Charles H. Zahn's Drug Store.

A good deal of my business was in leeches. . . . I imported a thousand of these [Swedish] leeches every month. The American leeches were too small. . . . Yes, on Second and Walnut, we had the leech trade of the city—Richardson Drug, Collins Brothers and Meyer Brothers bought leeches from me. . . . Meyer Bothers sold many porcelain leech jars in those days. . . . When people would come to my store and ask for relief on the "morning after" I sold them this Hunyadi Janos Water, which consisted of Epsom Salts, Glauber's Salts, and Chloride of Soda.

Quinine sold for $2.00 or $2.50 at most an ounce. I had a quack-doctor practicing near my store, and he prescribed Quinine for practically everything. . . . But with the coming of the Civil War, quinine jumped to $5.00 an ounce.

There were many kinds of pills on the market at that time. I made my own by rolling them out [as a mass], pushing the cutter over them, then [when subdivided] twirling them to make them round. I remember well making Kaiser pills, Plumbers pills, and Scammony pills.

The slogan of my store at the Barnum Hotel was "We Sell Everything."

William L. DuBois (b.1835-d.1913), Catskill, New York, 1863-1916

In the spring of 1851 I was attending the school of the Collegiate Reformed Dutch Church in New York. On leaving school one day my teacher . . . asked if I would like to take a position in an wholesale drug house. . . . I went home, talked the matter over with my father, and I concluded to go down town and make an application for the place. . . . After a long talk [with James L. Schieffelin of Schieffelin Bros. & Co.] I was engaged at a salary of $50 a year, and given a small desk in a corner office. . . .

[Eventually] I was put in charge of the city counter sales where the goods were put up. . . . I remained in the same position till March, 1863, when Mr. Benjamin Wey, whom I had known for a long time as an old customer of the House, made me a proposition to go in business with him in Catskill, and I accepted, arriving there on the last day of February, 1863, which fell on a Saturday that year. On Monday morning I came to the old store which had been established in 1795, . . . remodeled in 1861, and at that time was considered one of the finest up-to-date stores on the Hudson River. . . . The firm was "Wey &

DuBois" for thirteen years, when Mr. Wey retired, after a very pleasant business relation, in 1876.

Since then [I have] conducted the business, but what a change! When I came to Catskill in 1863, we did an extensive business in paint, putty, and window glass, dye woods, potash, and Lorillard's snuff. Every farmer's wife in the fall would get in her supply of extract of logwood, cochineal, muriate of tin and indigo, and would send her wool to little fulling mills, which were to be found on nearly every stream, to be carded, and she would do the spinning of the yarn and the dyeing during the winter. . . . Another great trade was potash. Every family at that time made their own soft soap and it did not take [us] long to be rid of a seven-hundred-pound cask of potash. . . . People are using the aniline dyes in place of making their own, and there are few now who make their own soap. In the old days we sold . . . probably as much as a ton [of snuff] in the course of a year, . . . now [1916] we sell only about two hundred fifty pounds in a year, quite a falling off as the younger generation have not followed in the footsteps of their grandparents in regard to that habit. We used to supply the country stores with essence of peppermint, wintergreen and castor oil and extract of lemon and vanilla. The railroads and the commercial travelers have changed all that now. The doctors carry their own medicines and put up their own prescriptions, except where there are ointments, liniments or suppositories to be made, we druggists get those. It is the [large-scale] manufacturing of tablets that has hurt the prescription business and made it easier for the doctors [to dispense]. One can hardly recognize the business of to-day as compared to fifty years ago.

John N. Hurty (b. 1852-d. 1925), Indianapolis, Indiana, 1870s

Col. Eli Lilly beguiled me into the drug business. I was a callow youth of 16 years and 9 months, and was to graduate in high school in the spring of 1870. Col. Lilly . . . was raking his yard . . . and I . . . was trudging unwillingly to school. "Hey, John," said the Colonel, and I stopped. "Come in here, won't you, I want to speak to you." I went in and he unfolded his story which shaped my life work. Up to that time it had never entered my mind to become a druggist. . . . All that day and the next, and the next, and for two weary weeks until school

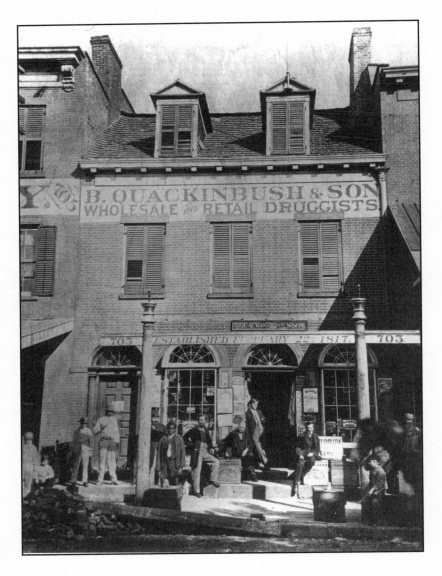

The facade of "B. Quackinbush & Son, Wholesale and Retail Druggists" in New York City, 1880, looking much as it had for decades past. (Photo courtesy of the Museum of the City of New York.)

ended, I thought, I dreamed, I contemplated becoming a druggist. . . . I walked by the Red Front Drug Store (that was the name of the Colonel's Emporium of drugs and simples) at least twenty times a day. My salary was to be three dollars a week and what could I not do with such a princely income? Priorly I had earned one fifty a week selling and carrying papers, and here was a jump of one hundred percent. . . . The morning of the first day I awoke at four and it seemed and interminable time until 6:30 A.M. . . . I was there twenty minutes before time. . . .

The Colonel appeared a little behind time. . . . The door opened and supposedly my life work was before me.

"Sprinkle the floor and sweep out" were the orders, and willingly I went at it. . . . The show cases, the counters and the base board of the shelves were then dusted with a feather duster and the store was ready for business. "Fix the lamps," was the next command. . . . But alas, I fell off the shaky step-ladder, broke both of the vitreous dispensers of light, skinned my shins and made an awful mess. . . . The Colonel was startled and he exclaimed, "My God, what a stupid ass you are," But . . . he relented and broke into a spasm of laughter. My life was saved.

In about two weeks I had another accident. . . . On the stairs I slipped and the end of the bundle [I was carrying] fell with heavy impact upon the bay rum bottle and shattered it into a million pieces. The bay rum poured forth upon my head and down my neck, saturating me with its fragrance. . . . [Eventually] we all broke out in laughter. . . . I was saved. . . .

Condition powders sold splendidly fifty years ago. We made our own and the "Red Front Lilly Condition Powders" had a reputation which was not bounded by county lines. I have made barrels and barrels of these condition powders and packed thousands of cartons. . . . The copperas, alum and rosin had to be powdered and the cub powdered them [a barrel of each] in a fifty-pound iron mortar and sift[ed] [them] through a fine sieve. It certainly is some job. The iron pestle had a hickory extension attached to a heavy cord which passed through a pulley overhead and was counterbalanced with a small sack partly filled with stones. Oh! the dust!. . . .

Baking powder was another great seller at the Red Front Drug Store. Making it was a clean but dusty job. When a batch was finished and placed in its paper-lined barrel, I was white as a miller, and again mouth, nose, ears, eyes and hair were fully, completely and absolutely filled and saturated. . . .

Has anyone under fifty ever made Dovers Powder? I doubt it. . . . Well, I have made it by Colonel Lilly's method. First the potassium sulphate and the powdered opium were stirred in a mortar for one-half hour, scraping down with a broad limber spatula. Finally, the compound was placed on a large sheet of paper and again mixed and mixed with a spatula. . . .

Patent medicines simply were on the rampage in my early drug store days. And yet—today, we find school teachers and preachers who have not risen out of the patent medicine stage of ignorance. Fifty years ago Helmbold, Jayne and other patent medicine kings wallowed in wealth. . . . Helmbold's great fortune was produced from nothing. Absolutely nothing. No, I am wrong, it was based upon the stupidity, ignorance, superstition and irrational credulity of mankind. . . .

Did you ever see a one-hundred pound box of asafetida in a little country drug store? . . . Well, the Lilly Red Front Drug Store, actually bought the malodorous drug in one hundred pound lots, and we powdered much of the vile stuff in a big iron mortar. In those days every child was a stinker because of a little bag of asafetida suspended over its chest. It was a rank stupidity, crass ignorance and silly, but it was done by Christian people. Several times in my early drug store experience I grew faint-hearted and seriously thought of engaging in some life work that had fewer . . . tiring and repugnant features. . . .

I wonder if there are any pharmacy kids . . . who ever spread split-skin plasters, made compound cathartic pills by the quart, and cut ten-pound lots of tamarind, fig and senna lozenges, or made pecks of cough troches? . . . My first batch of tamarind, fig and senna lozenges brought upon me a mighty catharsis for despite warning I persistently nipped off pieces of the mass to satisfy the gustatory pleasure hidden therein.

I watched Colonel Lilly spread a plaster with a curiosity that developed into great admiration. First, the white split skin was carefully squared, then tacked to a pine board and strips of calendered paper pasted around the edges. . . . Then the Colonel carefully spread the melted plaster mass with a spatula, finishing the surface to perfect smoothness. Then came the dusting with tartar emetic, and lastly the paper strips (the paste not yet dry) were skinned away and there was the finished product. . . . I was a proud pharmaceutic kid when I finally could turn out a pitch plaster which would pass inspection. . . .

Yes we had a Tufts Fountain, and after I had learned how to make syrups and charge fountains I voted it a nuisance. On circus days and at county fair time, people stood in line to drink our soda water, which had the reputation of being the best in town. . . .

In 1873 I attended the Philadelphia College of Pharmacy, and when I returned the Colonel one day remarked, "Well, I suppose you know it all now?" . . . "No," I said, "I don't know it all, but I know more than I would have under your teaching." "Good, Good," he shouted. "You'll come through."

Fred B. Kilmer (b. 1851-d. 1934), New York City & nearby New Jersey, 1870s

My first drug store job was washing bottles in the cellar, to the accompaniment of strenuous lectures because I put water in some of them before shaking out the straw. Surreptitiously, I watched the head clerk roll pills and make tinctures. (Boys were kept to work and not to learn pharmacy.) Finally, a kind-hearted partner gave me George Fownes' *Elementary Chemistry* to read, and kept me after the store had closed to explain it to me.

My wages were two silver dollars per week. The other day I met a chap who said he refused a drug clerkship because the wages were only sixty dollars a week. Our store was open sixteen hours out of the twenty-four. I opened it in the morning, and was on deck when the shutters were put up at night. Sweeping, scrubbing, cleaning show cases, shelfware and windows was my job. Now porters, with electric scrubbers and vacuum cleaners, do the real work, and the natty clerk comes in at nine in the morning, dons a white coat, and takes it off at five in the afternoon. Easy job—easy money.

As recently as the late 70's, with good credentials in my pocket, I tramped over New York City for days and days, east and west, north and south, from the Battery to Union Square (the extent of the retail section), seeking vainly for a job carrying the privilege of attending the school of pharmacy. Nobody wanted to bother with a clerk who had in his head highfalutin ideas about pharmacy being a profession. The job I finally landed gave me half a day and two evenings to attend lectures. For wages, I received my board with the boss, and the privilege of sleeping in the store. . . .

Gone are the good old days of free trade in [narcotic] poisons [for example:] We had a venerable lady customer who claimed to have gone well past the century mark. She smoked incessantly, drank coffee continuously, and consumed eight fluid ounces of laudanum each week. Moral: to live long, use stimulants and narcotics to excess. [And there was a] doctor who patronized our store got away with a bottle of morphine each of the 365 days in the year. Another day a girl of about eighteen came in, and without question I sold her four ounces of tincture of opium. Within an hour afterwards, two doctors and myself were mounted on horseback (there were no motor cars) speeding post haste with emetics and a stomach pump. . . .

James Hartley Beal (b. 1861-d. 1945), Uhrichsville, Ohio, late 1870s

In addition to the formulas in the United Stated Dispensatory, which we generally followed, [my employer W. W.] Alexander had some <u>quite</u> original ones of his own. One was for laudanum, . . . made by placing a "handful" of the crude [opium] "gum" in a half-gallon bottle and filling the vessel with cheap whiskey. After standing a few days, with occasional shaking, the tincture was ready for dispensing. . . .

Tincture of arnica was made in the same way, measuring by the handful, and using whiskey [as a menstruum] instead of alcohol and water. Tincture of ferric chloride was compounded by placing scraps of old iron, the more rusty the better, in a crock with commercial muriatic acid. When the acid was saturated, the liquid was filtered, then diluted with whiskey until . . . about the right color, determined by comparing it with the last batch.

Strange to say, Alexander's laudanum and tincture of iron were great favorites with the country physicians for miles around.

Jacob A. Flexner, Louisville, Kentucky, c. 1874-1893

. . . Until the panic of 1873 and the ensuing business depression completely ruined my father financially . . . my hopes were set upon medicine, [but] my only chance to realize them would now be to enter the profession by way of a drug store. . . . I secured a situation with Dr. Thomas E. Jenkins, who owned two drug stores. It was agreed that I should work for six months without remuneration; at the end of that period, if I proved my ability, I was to be rewarded with the munificent salary of ten dollars a month.

The store in which I began apprenticeship had an underground hallway lined with rows of shelves. Here were kept the heavier drugs and the excess of stock which was not required in the store above. Off this dark passage ran another hallway five feet wide and hardly more than six feet high. This was my bedroom.

Dr. Jenkins was himself a graduate in medicine and had been trained in chemistry . . . , with a keen appreciation of the distinction between science and pseudo-science. Accurate to a most unusual degree, he possessed qualities which inspired his customers with complete confidence; just to watch him wrap up a package of Epsom salts convinced one that it was the best Epsom salts in the world. . . .

At first I was put to work washing bottles and windows, but it was not long before I was promoted to the prescription counter, where I became an assistant analyst and pharmacist. Here I helped perform many tasks which I have never seen repeated in any latter-day drug store. We often prepared ores for assay and conducted many analyses that would now [1930] be undertaken by governmental agencies. . . .

Those were the days when the sale of harmful drugs was not restricted. I could relate many instances to illustrate the deplorable conditions which brought the Harrison [narcotics] law into being. . . .

Fifty years ago [c. 1880] no first-class pharmacist would have thought of depending up the great manufacturing firms to supply his tinctures, fluid extracts and capsules. We manufactured our own. . . . We purchased our ammonia and our sulphuric acid in carboys, our sulphur, cream of tartar, and lampblack in barrels. . . . We were taught the botany as well as the pharmacology of the *materia medica*, and in a small way the therapeutics as well. . . .

To symbolize their profession, pharmacists could choose among a dozen styles of showglobes offered in wholesale catalogs by the late nineteenth century. Ever more elaborate designs evolved from the simple grace of the utilitarian carboys used for bulk liquids by earlier apothecaries. The display carboy at left has been ornamented with a cut-glass stopper. (Photos courtesy of the Smithsonian Institution and The Upjohn Company.)

More than once my knowledge of drugs was the means of saving physicians from their own mistakes. In those days we had no telephones and it was often impossible to communicate with the doctor if we suspected an error in one of his prescriptions. At such times I had either to take the liberty and the risk of correcting the prescription myself or, by letting it go through, to expose the physician [to risk]. . . .

After three years of clerking in the drug store an offer came to me to take charge of the prescription manufacturing department of a much larger business. . . . In this place there was an air of the patent medicine; the proprietor seemed to think of nothing but the volume of his business. Here many things were purchased from the manufacturing pharmacists which I had formerly been accustomed to produce myself. . . . Most of my memories of this establishment are not pleasant.

. . . At my third job as a druggist's assistant I still took advantage of every opportunity to carry on medical studies. . . . By studying at night I had been able to take my degree from the College of Pharmacy. Now I was qualified to go into business for myself. . . . One of the oldest established drug stores in Louisville was for sale. . . . From the first my business was devoted almost exclusively to the filling of prescriptions written by physicians. With the reputation I had established in the stores where I had previously worked, it was not long before I was doing a thriving business. In the course of the next year I was able to pay off practically the entire debt upon the store.

Before long I had several graduates in pharmacy working with me. By interest and industry we developed a considerable business in what now passes under the name of "clinical microscopy". . . . Our new prescription department occupied the second floor. . . . The clerk [i.e., pharmacist] who had charge of this department had under him two graduates in pharmacy and several other helpers. . . . I preferred to manufacture my own drugs when possible, . . . produced practically all of my own tinctures and fluid extracts and many of the solid extracts from the crude [botanical] drugs. . . .

In 1893, I began formal studies in medicine . . . at the University of Louisville. The demonstrator of anatomy was a close friend and he allowed me many special privileges so that I might continue my work at the drug store, . . . among other things, to work at my dissections late at night long after the departure of the class. . . . In my later years it has interested me greatly to note that numbers of physicians of my generation, many of them highly distinguished, entered their medical careers as I did—through the drug store. With the modern tendency to make of a drug store anything rather than a drug store, this avenue is now closed to the medical student. Pharmacy is, indeed, a vanishing profession.

B. C. Huger, St. Louis, Missouri, 1870s?-1912

At fourteen I managed to secure a job with Thomas Layton at Grand and St. Louis Avenues. Mighty glad to get the job at three dollars a week—no definite day off. . . . Mr. Layton was a pharmacist of "the old school" and had about every kind of pharmaceutical apparatus listed in Whitall Tatum's catalogue. He made his own fluid extracts and tinctures. We put up Seidlitz powders by the thousands, Compound Licorice Powder [in bulk], and we even made our own Burnt Alum. The only objection to this was that it was my job to reduce the burnt Alum to a powder in an iron mortar and then run it thru a very fine sieve. . . . Ointments were dispensed in yellow or white earthen pots covered with parchment paper tied on as a cover. Most pill boxes were round.

We made our own carbonated water simply by rocking a tank of water while liquid carbonic gas was slowly introduced. Soda fountains usually had a thirst inciter which consisted of a large inverted bell glass with a stream of water [inside] forcibly hitting against the top. . . . The globe usually contained a risqué figure of a bathing beauty, or of a child with an umbrella.

Telephone wires in many parts of the city were strung from house to house; the instruments were very crude. . . . Transportation in St. Louis was slowly changing from the old-fashioned horse cars to cable cars. . . .

Because of the many crude drugs handled, the stores had a typical "drug store smell," and small, colored show-globes were a must as an identifying symbol. . . . A counter scale or balance much in evidence.

. . . It was customary to wrap a lot of five and ten cent packages of Prepared Chalk to be used for either face or tooth powder. Powder No. 40 Carmine sold instead of rouge. A great deal of Fennel seed and

German Chamomile was sold. . . . Orris root was sold for teething babies. Stick licorice was bought in hundred pound lots, which came packed in Bay Leaves. . . .

Mr. Layton was a distinguished appearing gentleman, . . . a great fighter for what he stood for in Pharmacy and Civic matters. After graduating from the St. Louis College of Pharmacy, I found that I was a supernumerary, so sought a position with W. D. Temm, a neighboring druggist—staying with him five years. My job was to sleep in an ante room of the store and answer night calls. We were called upon for all kinds of things, from a postage stamp to filling prescriptions. . . . It was not unusual to be called up for a dime's worth of paregoric or Powdered Mustard and a fiddle string, the latter being probably the most important. We handled Leeches and oftentimes were called on to apply them.

Mathias Noll, (b. 1859), Atchison, Kansas, 1880-1920

After forty years in the drug business, my great regret is that the drug store, the kind in which I learned to be a pharmacist, has lost its identity and that the character it once had is no longer recognizable. It is impossible for me to reconcile the fact that Pharmacy as a profession, which I spent so much time and money to learn, and years of experience as an active druggist to perfect, could have completely changed complexion. . . .

No other type of store could compete with the old-time drug store in human interest. A grocery store had a stomach, but the old drug store had a heart in it. In sickness, health, pleasure, woe or leisure, the drug store had no rival. It seemed that there was something in the sign of the Apothecary that made people want to go into a drug store whether they wished to buy or not. There they found the touch they could get nowhere else; to spend a few waiting minutes was a privilege not so valued in any other place. What appealed to them most, we druggists could only imagine from the pleased expression on their faces. We didn't know but that they came in because of the aroma of good cigars in the case, the odor from the sweet-scented soaps and perfumes, the gold fish, the long rows of pretty bottles of uniform size (containing medicines, of course), all lettered in gilt, which were kept on the shelves. . . .

Contrasting scenes in front of two Midwestern drugstores, 1860s and about 1910. They suggest a major change in access to pharmacy services that the newfangled motor-carriages seemed to promise. (Photo (Big Falls, WI) courtesy of Wisconsin Historical Society; woodcut from The Northwestern Family Medical Almanac, *Chicago: A. L. Scovill, 1870.)*

There is a tinge of sadness in the thought, and I can't quite realize it to be true, that the place I once owned and operated for forty years, known to all men as a drug store, is no longer in existence. I have a hard time explaining to my young grandchildren the difference between the drug store I sold less than twenty years ago and the one they see to-day [1930s]. I can imagine them telling me that they don't see anybody at the store doing things in the way I said I used to do them. . . .

Edward Kremers (b. 1865-d. 1941), Milwaukee, Wisconsin, c. 1885

Early in the 1880s I was seriously involved in the collecting of beetles and other natural things and often went to Louis Lotz's *Apotheke* to have Wickersham's solution prepared. I used it to preserve lizards, snakes, and other soft animal tissue. When a few years later, very American-like, I sought to become self-reliant and gave up my studies, my father suggested that I become an apothecary's apprentice, for I did not want to give up my studies in the natural sciences. An apprenticeship under Louis Lotz seemed to offer the only possibility of continuing these interests.

The shop was open from 7 in the morning to 10 at night. We were free two evenings a week and every other Sunday. Many times there was nothing to do after 9 o'clock or even earlier and we would sit around the table and desk and record our laboratory work in notebooks. Or we would prepare ourselves to handle the drugs most likely to be in demand the next day, while we were reading in Hager [*Handbuch der pharmazeutischen Praxis*] or some other scientific pharmaceutical work. Not infrequently, Mr. Lotz joined us, bringing a bottle of a light Rhine wine. Over glasses of the now forbidden nectar [this was written in 1923, during Prohibition] he solved our problems. A well-traveled man, he did not limit himself to technical matters. He drew upon much of the rich treasure of his experiences and gave a more humanistic slant to his technical and scientific explanations.

On Sundays I was on duty with the master. We were not idle on these days of rest. Although we paid attention only to what was necessary, we did not stand at the windows with our hands in our pants pockets gawking at the street traffic. In the morning new dispensing claimed our time fully. In the afternoons, however, we had a different pleasure, for then Mr. Lotz would become involved with his hobbies. Collections were arranged and every single object was lovingly doted over. In the process I received many a private lesson. . . . The very rich collections of the Lotz Apothecary introduced me personally to countless objects of all three of the natural kingdoms. I had not known before that the mineralogist Kobell wrote sonnets, and that the Court Apothecary Pettenkoffer was a universal genius, not to speak of Liebig and Buchner. But their influence made itself felt, not only through the presence of their pictures and their scientific works in the bookcase, but also through their student—Lotz, our Master Apothecary. He was also a many-sided genius, not only scientist and lover of nature, but artist also. What he did was not only *lege artis* in the sense of the art of the apothecary but art in its broadest sense.

Carrie Emily Howard, Philadelphia, Pennsylvania, 1886-1890

Excerpt from a student essay submitted at the Philadelphia College of Pharmacy, where Howard earned a diploma as "Graduate in Pharmacy" in 1890, after a 4-year apprenticeship with H. B. Snavely, Ph.G., M.D.

The woman question in relation to business has received much attention during the last twenty years. . . . Woman has enlarged her sphere of labor in a very marked degree, and has entered into mercantile and scientific life. . . . It is not presumptious to claim that many lines of business have special fitness for women and I think, of these, Pharmacy offers a great opportunity, being a sedentary indoor, neat, and clean business. . . .

Before assuming, myself, the business of a Pharmacist four years ago, I found my path [as owner] beset with many difficulties; . . . but I secured the services of a young and efficient Pharmacist and Physician, and devoting myself constantly to study and business methods, to-day I feel myself competent to stand alone, if necessary, and make my fight in the field of competition. . . . , and when I leave the dear old [Philadelphia] College of Pharmacy, where we have toiled with hands, feet, and brains, I hope that I may have my mind clear, and the way well opened for all the new things. . . .

I have had some amusing experiences. . . A short time since, I was putting up a Prescription for a gentleman (a new customer),

The drugstore soda fountain had become increasingly elaborate in both appearance and function during the half-century preceding this ornate model of the 1890s. Pharmacists recall a youthful apprenticeship that often included part-time service on the fountain. (Advertisement from The Pharmaceutical Era, *1 May 1891, 46.)*

who was waiting for it when an energetic and lively Irishwoman came in calling in a loud voice, "Is the Doctor in" I want a Prescription filled." I replied "No," inviting her to take a seat, saying I would wait upon her as quickly as possible. She sat but began a tirade upon the idea of allowing me to fill a Prescription, addressing herself to the gentleman who was waiting. I came forth with his Prescription in fear and trembling, expecting he would refuse to take it. He took it, however, and said: "Madam, I have every confidence in the ability of this pharmacist to do that which she had undertaken, and no doubt in the near future we will see many more women Pharmacists." The woman allowed me to put up her Prescription, and [later] became my most ardent partisan. . . .

On election day a red-faced red-nosed individual came in, saying "Give me eight ounces of whiskey." I told him it was impossible for me to do, without a Prescription. He said "Isn't this an Apothecary shop?" and went out, indignantly slamming the door—evidently a stranger from City or Town where the laws are more lax.

Scarcely a day passes without some amusing experience . . . , but then too we are called upon to listen to many sad tales of sickness and death; and who more capable than woman to extend a sympathizing word so dear to us in affliction? I hope the prediction of my male customer may be realized, that the day <u>will</u> come when many women will adopt the profession of pharmacy as their life work. . . . When I first entered the business [in 1886] there was a great distrust of me, and neighbors gave me only six months to remain in it, but it is a gratifying fact that each day lessens the prejudice against me as a Pharmacist.

John W. Gray, Detroit, Michigan, 1886-1914

Mr. Hurd and I commenced business at 208 Woodward avenue [Detroit] about the 1st of August, 1886, with a stock of drug mer-

A small-town Wisconsin pharmacy has features typical of the 1880s: a wooden floor and ceiling, gas lights and wood stove, pillared wall-cabinets filled with long rows of glass labeled salt-mouth and tincture-mouth bottles, and sundries displayed under glass. The prescription department is in the rear; front left is a small soda fountain; and in the center a single island-display offers candies. (Photo courtesy of F. and R. Bergmann, Watertown, WI.)

chandise and fixtures amounting to about $2500. We had a small soda fountain, and our stock consisted of drugs, patent medicines, perfumes, a few sundries, such as tooth, nail and cloth brushes, combs, shoulder braces, and a small stock of cigars. Until we began [price] cutting, along in 1894, Mr. Hurd and I, with the assistance of a boy, conducted the business.

Our average monthly sales during this period, with very little variation, were from $600 to $700, almost one-half of which we considered as gross profits. Rent was $100 a month, other expenses would total from $40 to $50 a month. Along in '94, as there had been more or less cutting of prices by our competitors, and our business had shown a slight loss for a few months, we decided to become more aggressive, and put on our signs and advertise ourselves as a cut-rate drug store. Our policy at the beginning was to meet prices made by any other house on anything in our line, and a price once established was continued indefinitely. . . .

As nearly as I can recollect, within six months from the time we began cutting prices, our average monthly sales had been doubled and the increase kept up at a gradually increasing rate until they became about $15,000 a month. . . . As our business was increasing, we put in a larger and more varied stock of sundries, rubber goods, fancy goods, cigars, etc. We also installed a new and large soda fountain, finding that our cut rates on patent medicines attracted many more people to our store and furnished the opportunity of increasing and expanding in many ways. On most of these goods we made the same profits as we had made under the old method of doing business. . . .

Josephine Wanous Stuart (1870-1936), Minneapolis, Minnesota, 1890-1912

I was brought up on a farm near Glencoe, Minnesota. While still in high school, I was employed in a local drug store as an interpreter (being of Bohemian parentage) and to sell books and stationery. From the first I was attracted by the black and red labels on the fluidextract bottles, and studied the labels with keen interest. . . .

After two years in the drug store I had become infatuated with the work, and went to the Minneapolis College of Pharmacy. I paid my own expenses with the money I had saved, partly by doing book-

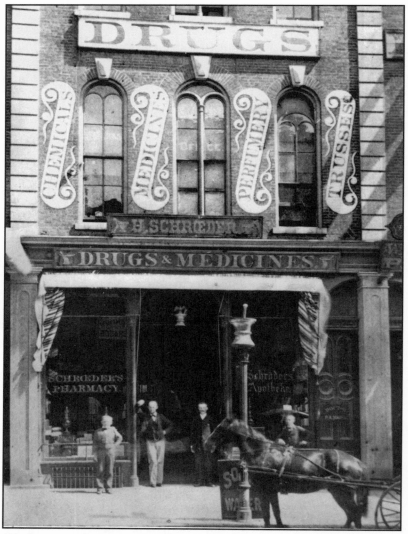

The American pharmacies of immigrant German pharmacists often were identified as a "Deutsche Apotheke," thus taking advantage of their repute for having a superior standard of practice. These two examples (above and right) are Schroeder's Apotheke (with English name opposite) in Quincy, Illinois, about 1880, and C. C. Sniteman's Deutsche Apotheke in Neillsville, Wisconsin, in the 1880s, which kept the German name until World War I. The influence of the Deutsche Apotheke is pointed up by the accounts of Joseph Lemberger, p. 54, and Edward Kremers, p. 99. (Quincy photo courtesy of Kenneth R. Lohr.)

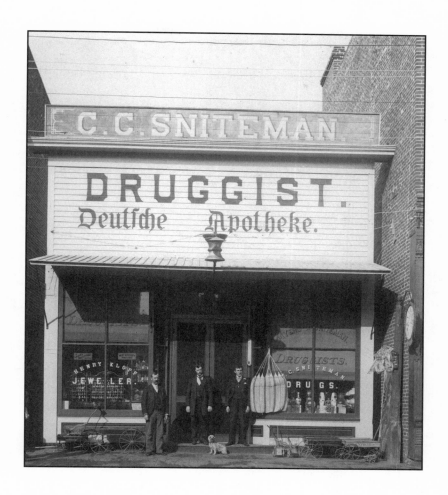

keeping in an office while pursuing my studies. I had tried dressmaking and millinery but disliked them both. My taste and talent were for chemistry. After graduation I passed the State examination and obtained my license.

Then my hardest struggle began. I went from drug store to drug store offering my services, but no pharmacist would employ a girl. Desperate for work and determined to remain in the city until a position offered itself in a drug store, I took a position to sell gloves in a large department store. The managers happened to be in difficulties with their man-manager in the drug department. After getting into [legal] trouble by dispensing medicines without having a registered pharmacist in charge, the pharmacist whom they secured was not at all satisfactory. In the floor manager's effort to get my pedigree he was very much surprised to learn of my pharmacist's license; so in less than two hours, I was placed in charge of the drug department with the advanced wages of two dollars a day.

I remained there for several years, but longed to work in a regular drug store. I finally gave up my position, with a salary of $50.00 a month, to take a month's engagement on trial in a pharmacy at $8.00 a week. I stayed there three years.

Then my sister urged me to set up in business for myself, even if I had to do it in a dry-goods box. So I rented two rooms on a second floor, and added to them as my business grew until I had seven [rooms]. From there I moved into a large store on Nicollet avenue.

While in the drug business, I was successful in securing a patent and placing on the market the little Wanous Shampoo-Bag, which has become popular in every State in the Union. I am no longer in the retail drug business, being interested in the Wanous Shampoo-Bag, and in a nice home and baby boy.

A. C. Meyer (b. early 1870s), St. Louis, Missouri, 1890s.

By June of 1891 my ambition was gratified [to join the family wholesale drug firm, Meyer Brothers Drug Company] and I reported for work. A fixed schedule was written out, advising when to move from one department to the next in order to gain a general knowledge of the operations. . . . Then it was not considered a requirement to make shipment of orders on the day they were received and only a small percentage were handled with such dispatch. Order sheets held in clips were taken out of the dumb waiter and placed before Mr. John Wilson, superintendent. Mr. Wilson would leisurely scan the orders, [and] indicate in various marks and letters from an assortment of colored leads such items as case lots, barrels, bags, etc., as carried in the warehouses. . . . Floor tickets of many shades indicating the particular department would be distributed by messenger boys, of which I was one for a while. . . . Only such young men who wrote legibly and were good penmen could qualify for this work. . . .

Drug cartons had not yet arrived and paper bags were not used to any extent if at all. It was necessary to weigh out drugs, chemicals, etc. as orders were being executed. If, for example, there appeared on the requisition Powdered Borax in two, five or ten pounds, or other subdivisions, the order filler would tear from the paper cutter the required size of white paper, placing this on the scale pan with a brass weight on the other pan corresponding to the amount to be weighed out. The item would then be scooped from the bins or drawers over a goodly section of the order department floor. . . . [When the drug was] folded neatly into the sheet of paper, a symmetrical package would be formed, tied with thin twine, then a second wrapper of a heavier paper held together with coarser twine. Printed labels had not yet been conceived. Instead, markings were made by means of pen and ink with a backhand stroke letter-shaded—really a masterful piece of work. . . .

The drug sundries department was located on the third floor. . . . Tremendous changes came about in the sundries line. Who can remember T. M. Shoe Blacking?. . . . Arnold's Ink packaged in clay jars of about one quart was imported from England in car lots. . . . Safety Razors had not been invented but we carried a wide variety of the old style. . . . Most retail sales [of perfumes] were measured out from bulk packages. . . . One of the first entries that appeared on the outfit order [of a new drugstore] before the turn of the century was a pair of Pine-

apple[-shaped] Show Globes; these were indispensable. Cork Presses, Leech Jars, Physicians' Cases, Saddle Bags, Chest and Lung Protectors, just to mention a few items at random, were regularly called for [in the '90s]. Wooden packing boxes and cases were the rule . . . The final entry on invoice was the charge for Boxing, and for Drayage when shipments had to be hauled to the various freight houses.

The large horse-drawn stake wagons [of our wholesale drug firm] delivered the out-going shipments, and the various railroad companies and the numerous express companies . . . also transported great quan-

Mass marketing, fueled by innovations in transport and communication, became a social problem as well as economic stimulus by the 1880s. Some manufacturers of remedies were exploiting unregulated advertising to the hilt. (Advertisement from Noyes Bros. & Cutler Catalogue. . . ., St. Paul, 1894.)

tities to the levee. Here the merchandise was carried by boat to the landings extending up and down the Mississippi, Missouri and Illinois Rivers. There were in those early days but a limited number of wholesale drug houses [except in the East], in consequence of which the St.

Louis [sales] territory extended over the greater portion of these United States. The traveling representatives of the jobbers covered their respective territories every sixty days or so, which meant that the orders consisted of numerous items in substantial quantities. . . .

The traveling representatives were then known as either drug salesmen or sundries men, the latter carrying an extensive line of druggists sundries, frequently requiring as many as a dozen large trunks to contain their samples.

(Copyright 1948, by Meyer Brothers Drug Company, St. Louis)

Frederick T. Gordon (b. 1870-d. 1917), United States Navy, 1890s-1912.

There have been such changes in the rank, status and duties of the naval apothecary since the days following the Civil War and there are . . . few of us old apothecaries left. . . .

The status of the naval apothecary in the early days was considerably different from that of today; then he was practically a civil employee, subject of course to naval discipline; now [1913] he is a member of a highly trained organized corps and an integral part of the personnel of the navy. Then the apothecary was appointed by the ship's medical officer for the "cruise" or such time as his services were needed; he was not required to enlist for any definite time and in fact often did not enlist at all but simply held his billet as ship's apothecary at the pleasure of the medical officer and captain of the vessel on which he served. . . . On shore the conditions were similar. The apothecaries of navy yards and hospitals were really civil appointees, they were not required to wear uniforms and had the same status as other civil employees in regard to tenure of office and discipline. . . .

This was the condition when I entered the navy in 1890. . . . These rather indefinite conditions were all changed by the Hospital Corps bill of 1898 which for the first time established a definite organization for the Hospital Corps of the Navy and made it a part of the regular navy personnel. The rank of pharmacist, that of warrant officer, was created by this bill and all apothecaries were required to enlist. . . . [It became] far more attractive to the young graduate in pharmacy than did the uncertain conditions and future of years ago. The present pay of the hospital steward, the title now given to the naval apothecary, is $70 a month, with an allowance for uniforms on original enlistment and the usual navy ration allowance of 30 cents a day.

Conditions of life aboard ship have changed. . . . The sick bay, the space set aside for the sick, was still usually a space in the very bow of the ship, separated from the crew's living quarters by a bulkhead; and the dispensary where the apothecary did his work was merely a small cell-like space either alongside the sick bay or somewhere on the berth deck out of the way. . . .

The dispensary . . . was a small space with a work counter on one side, above which were racks of bottles and, in drawers below, space for keeping various articles of stock and, on the other side, a locker with shelves. This locker usually had a folding seat, or sometimes a permanent ledge about a foot wide, where patients might be seated for examination during the day and on which the apothecary made his bed the best he could at night. . . .

Our supplies were very limited, mostly staple drugs and a few fluidextracts and tinctures. Pills when called for we made, capsules were a luxury only for the few, and "elegant" pharmaceuticals were unknown. In my first supplies I had fluidextracts made by Squibb as far back as 1870; but as they were never used, I had no idea of their efficiency at the age they then were. Everything was the simplest and crudest, the scales, for example, being the old style swinging balance on which it was impossible to weigh anything when the ship was at sea and rolling around. We got so skillful that we could guess weights within five or ten grains, and let it go at that, of course being more careful with potent drugs, morphine for instance, which I have known to be measured on the point of a knife blade in emergency. . . .

If our supply of one drug was exhausted we used the next best—until we could get fresh supplies, and the substitution that we had to do would shock an ethical pharmacist into his grave. Often I have made blue ointment and protoiodide of mercury from iodine and quicksilver.

Nowadays [1912] the sick bay of a battleship is like the ward of a modern hospital. . . . The dispensary is equipped with modern conveniences, even a typewriter now being usual, and the medical supplies are not only liberal in quantity but contain such items as diphtheria and typhoid antitoxins and most of the tested and approved remedies of the modern materia medica. In brief the difference [in navy pharmacy] is just about the same as between the old days in the drug store when the apothecary made everything and now everything is made for him.

The old naval apothecary was expected to be a good apothecary, a fair penman and a man of good general intelligence. . . . He was expected to have general supervision of the nursing of the sick and was generally the surgeon's assistant during operations and attended the minor cases, applied dressings, etc. In addition to all these duties the present day apothecary must have knowledge of modern hygiene and hospital practice, must be capable of performing chemical analyses, assisting in bacteriological examinations and must be thoroughly familiar with the various drills and practices incident to caring for the wounded. . . . Nowadays the battleship's equipment contains what is practically a complete chemical and bacteriological laboratory equipment. . . . My chief chemical work used to be testing the fresh water from the condensers to determine its potability. . . . There were occasional rough examinations of urine and once in a while a call for testing some article purchased ashore. And I had almost forgotten, so long ago has it been abandoned, a weekly testing of the air on the berth deck to determine the amount of carbon dioxide it contained. . . .

The present duties [1912] of the apothecary at shore stations and naval hospitals includes even more technical work than is required from him when aboard ship. In addition to having charge of the dispensary he has general supervision of the nurses and kitchens, acts as purveyor of stores, superintends the purchase of fresh meats, provisions, etc. and does the general bookkeeping of the station. He is often called on to make X-ray examinations, chemical analyses and assist in bacteriological work and at times to assist the surgeon as anaesthetist during operations. . . .

The life of the naval apothecary nowadays is far more comfortable and more pleasant than in the olden days. . . . In personal comforts things have changed for the better; the ventilation is good and the sleeping quarters of the apothecary is equipped with a comfortable bunk, he has electric lights to read by and can take a shower bath whenever he wants to.

William C. Alpers (b. 1851-d. 1917), Bayonne, New Jersey, 1890s

The Merck Pharmacy is moving along on the lines as originally contemplated; the difficulties, however, that have arisen and are still arising are greater than could be anticipated. That the greatest and most violent opposition against the mere existence of such an institution should come from the pharmacists themselves, and particularly from the Germans, is a sad sign. . . .

To push this new pharmacy, a long and tedious method has to be adopted and a systematic way of advertising to be followed. I visit from 3 to 5 physicians every day. . . . Sometimes I am received cooly and made to feel that a druggist is a poor specimen of a professional man; sometimes also the sins of pharmacy during the last 3 decades are condensed in a few words and sarcastically hurled at me; sometimes total indifference to all matters pharmaceutical. . . .

These visits take nearly the whole morning. Meanwhile my typewriter has written as many letters to other physicians, who live too far to be visited now. . . . I cannot help thinking that this work, although undertaken for purely selfish motives, will yet react beneficially on pharmacy in general; for I see every day that fully 50 percent of all physicians hear from me for the first time of pharmacy as a profession, and certainly some of them will change their ideas about our inferior position and standard. . . .

Besides this agitation among physicians I also try to educate the public in a similar way. You have seen my first booklet. . . . A second one is now in the press and will come out in January, being distributed in 10,000 copies.

Walter H. Cousins, [Sr.] (b. 1879), Central Texas, c. 1895-1915

I first saw the light in a little two-room shack at the edge of the old McKenzie cattle trail in 1879. My father was a typical pioneer who spent his life on the edge of the world. . . . Reared on the frontier, educated in the school of experience, I never attended high school or college.

My mother traded seven dozen eggs for the first horse I ever owned. . . . While I still ride the best horses in Texas, I recall with a thrill "Jake," the red roan, Spanish pony I had first. . . . I developed into a horse tamer and cow hand. . . . First job was with the M.N. Ranch as Bronc Buster and trail cook. On the trail we moved herds from Texas to Oklahoma, Kansas and to Montana and Canada. . . .

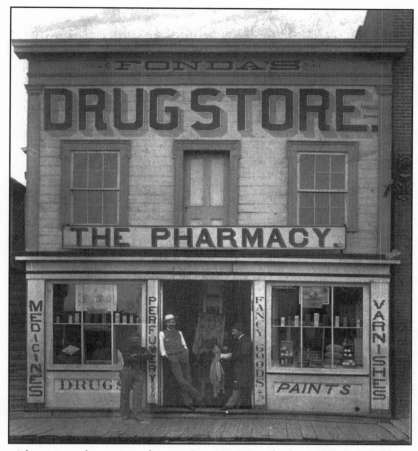

Adventurous pharmacists who went "out West" to make their mark sometimes practiced under conditions less than ideal. This drugstore in Boulder, Colorado, was owned by a Colonel George Fonda, who was lounging out front with friends when photographed in 1880. An East-coast pharmacist, John Best, who also settled in Colorado, recorded what it was like to practice there during the 1870s (p. 78). (Photo copyright Denver Public Library.)

If there had been a chuckwagon pharmacopoeia, it probably would have contained less than a half dozen items—not a matter of stinginess, but rather a matter of ignorance. . . . The men lived in the world of cattle and knew little else. A popular remedy for all external ailments was coal oil [kerosene]. For cuts, bruises, burns and what have you, it was used for both men and horses. In most chuck wagons

there was a can of turpentine, a bottle of paregoric, a bottle of camphor spirit, a jar of Epsom salts; and some chuck wagons also carried a
jug of whisky, thought to be a specific for snake bite. . . . This was the
prolific source of so many imaginary snakes that many trail bosses re-

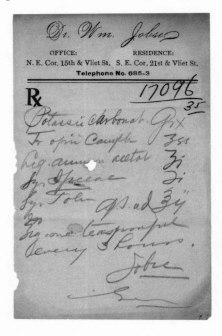

*Polypharmacy waned slowly
until drug therapy became
more specific, less symptom-
atic. This prescription,
probably from the 1890s,
combines three botanical
and two chemical
ingredients—probably as a
cold remedy. No patient
name or date was necessary.*

fused to carry it. . . . Much of the water on some trails necessitated an
occasional dose of paregoric. . . . However, we never heard of a paregoric addict among trail drivers.

Cowboys had the least medical attention of any craft of men that
ever lived. They were for the most part hundreds of miles from a hospital or a physician, and crude were many of the remedies they used.
The cook with a trail outfit was usually the nearest thing to a physician or pharmacist that could be found in the cattle country. . . . We
recall a cook who always carried green willow poles in his wagon;
when occasion demanded he burned these into charcoal, ground it in
his coffee mill, and poured it down the sick cowboys with a table-
spoon. . . . Another favorite for external use was axle grease, . . . made
for the lubrication of the axles of vehicles. . . . One of the best antisep-

tics to be had, it was used on men and horses for cuts, bruises, rope burns and saddle sores.

There were a number of medicinal plants that grew in the cattle ranges. One that was extensively used was the wild thyme, commonly called Horse Mint in the cattle country. The leaves and flowers, after being bruised in the hands, were used as an inhalant in head colds and hay fever. . . . Another plant which was extensively used was the balmony weed [*Chelone glabra*], which was made into a [purgative] infusion. . . . There was the loco plant [toxic species of Astragalus and Oxytropis], . . . called "Horse Cocaine" because the effect it had on a horse is similar to the effect on a human being. Coca leaves . . . wrapped around a [bone] felon . . . were supposed to relieve the pain. . . . The leaves of the Jimson Weed [*Datura stramonium*] were recommended [as a poultice] for boils. We think suggestive therapeutics ran

Even for a pharmacy of some professional pretension—such as this one photographed during the 1890s in Salida, Colorado—soda-fountain service was coming to seem essential. In contrast a stock of "simples" and their preparations (here in more than 200 glass-labelled shelf bottles) was coming to seem unessential, as mass-produced, packaged medicines poured from remote manufactories. Several reminiscences reflect practitioners' pain in having their traditional function preempted and "commercialized." (Photo copyright by Denver Public Library.)

The term "drummer" was in the American vocabulary by the 1860s. The drug drummer "Dr. Jack" was photographed while soliciting orders at Lucius Judson's drugstore in Michigan. Small-town druggists looked forward to periodic visits from the drummers, who brought colorful accounts of the wider world—and of new products. Pharmacist Shine Philips remembers (p. 120) their "flamboyant clothes, florid language, and brand new jokes." (Photo courtesy of E. S. Peer, Flint, MI.)

As the network of railroads expanded westward, it simplified life behind a drugstore counter by speedy replenishment of shelfstock from suppliers. It also brought an explosive expansion of marketing via traveling salesmen. In sizeable towns, a salesman such as Dr. Jack (at top) could ride a horsecar between the railroad station and a hotel or drugstore. The horsecar in Grand Junction, Colorado (bottom photo, 1887) also afforded Haskell's Pharmacy a new advertising opportunity. (Photo copyright by Denver Public Library.)

rampant around chuck wagons. . . . It was generally conceded by most of the men of the cattle trails that whisky was a specific for whatever ailed you. . . . There might have existed such [drugs] as acetanilid and bromides, but if they existed in Dodge City nobody knew about it. . . . The blessed paraldehyde was known in those days, but was unknown to those cattle valets who needed it most.

. . . I carried a pharmaceutical "library" on the top shelf of the chuck box. . . . Studying pharmacy and cooking three meals a day . . . was not a continual round of pleasure, especially when the outfit was moving five thousand three-year-old steers ten miles a day across the sage tussicks of Oklahoma. . . . One thing that made me quit cow punching, cooking and bronc busting was that I got tired of sleeping in the rain. I swore by the broken rope and bloody spurs that I would tackle some kind of a job that permitted me to sleep under a roof and eat "sittin" down. This could not be done in a cow camp. . . . The day I was 21 years old I told the well-known world that I would never roll another sour dough biscuit, climb on another bad horse, or have anything to do with cattle, but I could not quite live up to it.

. . . We mustered sufficient courage to ask Dr. Caleb L. Terrell of Haskell, Texas, for a job as an apprentice. . . . The Terrell store was a regular drug store, no soda fountain and no cigars, but every thing in the way of merchandise implied by the term drug store. . . . After negotiation we were permitted to stand around the store, and each Saturday night the doctor presented us with a blue envelope with four dollars in it. . . . I got board for $11 a month, slept over the store.

With hard study and much care we finally got so we could walk around the store without breaking anything, . . . then one fine morning woke up in the austere presence of the Board of Pharmacy where we sweated blood and made ninety [on the licensing exam].

In January 1900 we took $500 to Munday Texas and started our first drug store. It was about the size of a suppository box and our sales ran from nothing to as high as $20 in a day. We slept in the back room and had no clerks. The store was a plank shack, but by and by the country settled and the railroad came, and in this plank shack we have taken as high as $800 cash in one day. I stayed in the retail drug business 15 years, then in 1915 I bought the *Southern Pharmaceutical Journal* from Dr. E. G. Eberle, and for the last 17 years I have been busy with it. But I still hark back to the cattle country.

The great Southwest is now dotted with cities and towns, the dim trails have become ribbons of concrete. The fleet-footed Spanish pony has been supplanted by swiftly moving automobiles. . . . In the land of wide open spaces, the practice of pharmacy has kept pace.

Ernest L. Harris (b. 1874), St. Louis, Missouri, 1900-c. 1945

Many St. Louisans remember May 8, 1900, as the date of the bloody street car strike. The horse-drawn cars were overturned; and angry strikers pushed their way through the stream of work-bound pedestrians, . . . as the fourth largest city of the United States stirred itself for another day. At 23rd and Market Streets the doors of the drug store opened for my *first* day in business.

There was one other Negro drug store in the city at that time, on the corner of Jefferson Avenue and Morgan Street, owned by one of our prominent lawyers. By 1904 . . . Negroes owned four drug stores. All but one were within a few blocks of each other in the Negro area bounded by Jefferson Avenue on the west and the river on the east. The fourth store was in Elleardsville, a Negro neighborhood farther west. . . . As the Negro population drifted westward in the city, new stores were established and Negro pharmacists were employed in white stores in Negro sections.

Almost overnight the thinning downtown area was taxed beyond its housing capacity by the hundreds of Negroes who fled across the Mississippi River from Illinois following the flaming East St. Louis race riot in 1917. Fanatically race conscious as a result of their recent experience, these families threw their entire support to Negro enterprises; and the druggists (with the rest of the merchants) experienced an upsurge of trade that lasted throughout World War I. . . . The return of the soldier-druggists marked the beginning of the halcyon 1920s, when there was a great increase in the number of graduates, both men and women . . . Twenty-eight Negro drug stores were showing a substantial profit. It was a period of expansion that contrasted dramatically with the unparalleled depression of the following decade.

The St. Louis picture in the 1930s was one of closing stores, depleted inventories, and reduced staffs. This was the case everywhere in the country. About one-third of the drug stores survived; and this small group attempted to organize for strength in buying power by ordering as one unit from the wholesale houses. But the effort, like everything else in those devitalizing times, was dispirited and doomed to failure. Retrenchment was the order of the day until history completed the full cycle with the coming of World War II. . . .

The students of today and the "old grads" speak different languages. Techniques and terminology change as knowledge increases. Gone are the old prescription rooms redolent of aromatic herbs and spices or reeking with the pungent odors of camphor, ammonia, and iodoform, to name a few. Gone, too, are the weary man-hours grinding with mortar and pestle, pounding, stirring, shaking, mixing, sift-

Pharmacy's version of a "mom-and-pop store" was commonplace in American towns and cities until well into the 20th century. Nostalgic memories recall the drugstore as a congenial place, where family and townsfolk came together. That feeling is conveyed by this scene in a Milwaukee pharmacy on Teutonia Avenue about 1900. Between Pharmacist Henry Roemheld and his wife Fanny (behind the counter) are their two sons. (Photo courtesy of Irmgard Roemheld and Eunice Bonow Bardell.)

ing, folding, measuring, weighing, wrapping, labeling—in an endless routine that filled every spare moment between customers and made the [druggist's] old nickname "pill roller" far more meaningful then than now. No longer is the young druggist geared to an economy like that of the early 1900's in which costs and prices were reckoned in nickels, dimes, and quarters. He does not know how the very sight of the old, familiar red and green apothecary [show-]bottles causes the whole nostalgic past to unfold.

Shine Philips (b. about 1889), Big Spring, Texas, c. 1901-1925

Forty years ago [c. 1900] in Big Spring, Texas, a drugstore was a drugstore. We always bought epsom salts, sulphur and oils in large quantities and had a big stock of carbon disulphide on hand for the poisoning of prairie dogs. In a room at the rear of the store we bottled our castor oil, turpentine, and everything else we sold in small quantities. . . . The prescription department was a sacred place and a pharmacist got to be a pharmacist by the apprentice route, which meant a certain number of hours, days, nights, and years of working in a drugstore and reading Remingon's *Practice of Pharmacy* when there wasn't a customer around. By and by, the apprentice thought he knew enough and then he rode his horse down to the nearest town when the "District Board" met. . . . If the apprentice passed [its examination for a practice "Permit"], he put on a collar and tie and started deciphering the doctors' prescriptions behind the sacred prescription case.

Forty years ago the cosmetic business was in its embryo stage. A woman who wore rouge was a bad woman, and if she painted her lips she belonged to the devil sure enough. . . . Ten cents worth of prepared chalk "with just a small tint of pink, please" would last our fair damsels for months. There were three boxed face powders on the market but they were just for the rich and modern. . . . There weren't any powder puffs then either, but we did a flourishing business in chamois skins which the ladies made up into fancy powder rags or "shammies" to put on the prepared chalk with. . . . The girls took a square or oblong or round piece of chamois skin, sewed beading and ruffles of lace around the edge and ran ribbon through it. Sometimes they embroidered the edge with French knots and wrote verses on the chamois skin with ink in a fine Spencerian hand.

Sachet powders came in bulk too. We sold it by the dram and put it up in a pill box. . . . [Ladies put some] in their handkerchief drawer or in the collar boxes of their husbands. Mostly they sewed up dried lavender off the lavender bushes in little muslin bags to put [pleasant scent] in the sheets and pillow cases.

. . . When Mama came parading the baby buggy down the board walk, if Junior was big enough he climbed out over the side before she could steer the go-cart through the door, because he knew that Ma was going in after another stock of castor oil, asafoetida to tie up in a little bag and hang around his neck to keep off the measles and "hooping" cough, or for some of that yellow stuff [sulfur] she fed him in the spring mixed with molasses and cream of tartar into a repulsive mess.

The first soda fountain in our store was merely a hole in the counter. We put soda in the water, took some marble dust and added sulphuric acid to it, and that gave off the carbonic acid gas which collected in an outfit that had a little hose on it. This was connected to the drum that had the soda in it. This was "rocked" on what we called a "cradle" until the water was charged enough to taste a little like our present-day carbonated water. There was just about enough pressure to make it run up through a goose-necked tap which stood high on the counter. Many humorous explosions took place when the charge was too heavy.

Of course soda fountains improved rapidly and by and by we had one that had a wonderful standing lamp in the middle with glass-

A busy Midwestern drugstore in 1902, the Miller & Arthur Drug Co. in Quincy, Illinois. (Photo courtesy of Kenneth Lohr.)

The health-giving properties attributed to mineral water spas gave rise to artificial mineral waters by the 1850s, and to dispensing devices for drugstore counters, such as Nichols Mineral Water Fountain (left). At first limited to soda water, the small units evolved into elaborate soda fountains. As a variety of pleasant beverages became popular, tables for fountain service often were crowded into a drugstore corner, as in this congenial scene at Heimstreet's Drugstore, Janesville, Wisconsin, in 1902.

bead fringe all around; and we even put in a few tables and some of those wire chairs which were the pride of early soda fountains and ice cream parlors, and guaranteed to give you curvature of the spine. . . .

We didn't have a cash register in our drugstore, so the cash was kept under the showcase in a drawer that opened when you placed your first and third fingers on certain gadgets underneath the drawer. . . . [Although] Mr. Reagan had no way of checking on the honesty of his employees . . . there wasn't much stealing. Dishonesty just wasn't countenanced in those days, whether on the range, or in a poker game, or behind the counter.

The drugstore has always been the chief meetingplace of the Hot Stove League, and that's the way it was with ours in Big Spring. This is probably because it opens first in the morning and closes last at night. All the male gender of the town came to the drugstore to unload their troubles and sound off their opinions. . . . All the political confabs were held in the store but I doubt if any of the arguments and orations that took place there had much effect on the fate of the nation. The drugstore was the common meeting ground of all kinds of people. . . . The "Whittlin' Crew" were all old-timers with various ailments, but they usually managed to get home in time for meals. They always met at the store each morning. . . .

Big Spring doctors, in those happy times, believed in pills and they prescribed them. We made them up in the drugstore by hand, by forming a pill mass made of some sticky substance like a combination of gums and inert powder to give bulk. This mass held the drugs . . . and we rolled this mass into a long thin cylinder, cut it in equal parts, and then pill-rolling began. We rolled each pill between our fingers and then placed the pills in a cylindrical wooden or metal cup and rotated it to give the pills uniform roundness. They then were coated in a liquid made of sugar and water and rolled out on oiled paper to dry . . .

Quinine was widely prescribed, and while we had few malarias or fevers in this high dry climate, it was believed to be good for everything. Everybody took quinine in the winter to prevent something— God only knew what. Some people just put it in their shoes. Epsom salts, camphor, sweet spirits of nitre, and well aged whiskey were part of the doctor's dispensary. . . . Morphine was the doctor's stand-by. It was also sold over the counter. . . .

With the advent of affordable color printing, "trade cards" became a popular form of promotion during the late-19th century in many kinds of stores, not least in the drugstore. Pharmacists often received supplies of such cards from manufacturers of self-medication products. Here one example advertises a toothache remedy featuring cocaine, then used as an effective local anesthetic, with or without prescription. Another typical card exploits the fear among 19th-century laity of harboring intestinal worms, as well as the public's fascination with native Indian remedies. (From the William H. Helfand Collection.)

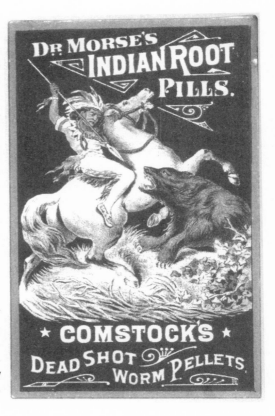

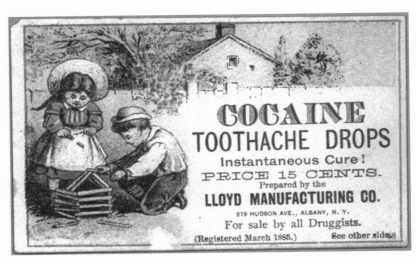

Diphtheria was one of the scourges of children in those days and it was called every thing from membranous croup to tonsillitis. It was treated with hot bricks and mustard plaster because this was before antitoxin came into general use. There is no way of knowing the dreadful mortality rate then, as its diagnosis was often in doubt. Scarlet fever was often fatal and usually left those who got well maimed in some way. There was no serum for it and the disease just had to run its course. Smallpox ran roughshod over communities and people feared it more than anything. Quarantine was rigidly enforced. . . .

Drug drummers were on the top rung of magnetism [among the traveling salesmen]. They were hard-working men who had to pack an awful load of samples. . . . When they came to town they stayed several days . . . , to rest their horses and give the local maidens a real treat. Sometimes they would hire a hack in one town and drive it to the next and leave it and hire one there and go to the next town. A drummer coming from the other direction would pick up their hack and drive back to the livery stable it belonged to. But the successful ones owned their own teams and hacks. They used to come spanking into town behind a team of bays with their harness ajingle, like the lords of creation. . . . They had flamboyant clothes, florid language, and brand new jokes—jokes for men only.

(Copyright 1942, by Prentice-Hall, Inc.)

Roy Bird Cook (b. 1886-d. 1961), West Virginia, 1905

In May 1905 [at age 19] I received a letter from the West Virginia Board of Pharmacy telling me that I had successfully passed the examinations for a registered pharmacist. . . . What was this new world into which I had elected to spend my life? Let us take a look at a typical pharmacy of 1905. . . . It was in a good location, fairly well lighted with [coal] oil lights which had to be trimmed, or with gas lights which had porcelain tips or jets. Few had installed the new-fangled electric lights.

And what of the sign outside the shop? Nearly all [?] had a post on the curb with the mortar and pestle gracing the top. . . . Also those who remember the cigar store's Indian with raised tomahawk, or the harness shop's horse on wheels, will also remember the drug store's life-sized figure of a down-east fisherman, painted and varnished in glowing colors, protected by an oil skin coat and hat, bearing on his back a cod fish. Each morning a pharmacist or his errandboy pulled this effective advertising of Scott's Emulsion [of cod-liver oil] out onto the sidewalk. . . . [Inside] along one wall was the soda fountain, probably made by Tufts of Boston, its design copied from some ancient temple. Here also reposed patent medicines, now long forgotten, which cured everything, and some Swans Down face-powder for any lady brave enough to buy it.

The store owner who could afford a Bang's-from-Boston set of store fixtures owned the showplace of the town. Manufacturers vied to see which could use the finest mahogany and plate glass in their fixtures. No pharmacy worthy of the name was without a complete set of fine hand-made tincture and powder bottles [on open shelves] which ran clear along one side of the store . . . [with] the fine-herb section on the bottom shelves. . . .

The pharmacist, who usually wore a black alpaca coat, presided. He was not above doing a little doctoring himself. He could recite stories of other days or repair a bruised toe. Irvin Cobb once observed that "nothing ever happens in a small town," then produced evidence to show that everything happens in just such places and especially in the town drug store. . . .

In the rear of such stores in 1905 one found real pharmacies. Jars of glycerite of starch stood on the marble prescription cases, from which pills or soft-mass capsules were compounded. Big scales and little scales were on the counter, and behind them stood *Remington's Practice of Pharmacy*, the *Dispensatory*, and often other books on drugs. Along the top shelves were boxes of the finest ground barks and herbs from the Baltimore market. . . . Can any remember the curious gourds [filled with dried juice] of aloes that had to be broken with a hammer, . . . or the arnica flowers to be bruised and packed in the right menstruum [for percolation], or the wonderful perfume of vanilla beans which had to be cut up with scissors, pounded in the big mortar, then made into choice extract! . . . This gives a fairly accurate picture of the store where I started as a pharmacist fifty years ago.

Here prescriptions for the sick, written by the family physician, were filled by the gentle hands of the family druggist. These prescriptions, thousands of which are still filed away in basements, could tell many interesting facts. . . . In my own files, I have today [1955] such prescriptions for four and five generations of one family in my home town. But what of the drugs? This was the age of vegetable drugs. . . . [But] in 1903 a new drug with a long chemical name [benzoyl-acetyl-peroxide], commonly known as Acetozone, had come on the market. It assailed typhoid fever and was a new venture in the field of pharmacy. . . . Anti-Diphtheric Serum had been discovered but was not yet in general use. There was no insulin, emetine, or adrenaline, and we had not yet heard of arsphenamine. X-ray, now sixty years old, was just coming into use, and radium [therapy] was unknown. Think what it meant to be druggists . . . to help minister to the sick without these helps.

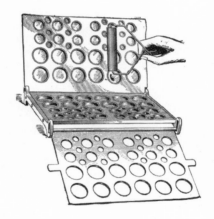

George H. Balloff (b. 1884-d. 1975), New York, New York, 1907-1960

I arrived in the U.S.A. in 1905 at the age of 21. . . . After a short time I enrolled in night school. . . . There was a pharmacy across the street from the school [and] one day I went in to purchase a stamp. The owner, a pleasant fellow, detected my Russian accent immediately, and being a Russian himself, was glad of the opportunity to renew his familiarity with his native tongue. After a pleasant talk he offered me a job as an apprentice, which I gladly accepted. I was very proud of myself. Here I was, I thought, speaking to a real pharmacist with my hat on yet. In Russia you would not dare to enter a pharmacy with your

Drugstore glassware often was ornamental as well as functional. This ring-jar, with three separable compartments, graced many a counter during the second half of the 19th century. Each compartment would be filled with bulk candies (such as horehound or licorice), packets of sachet powder, or other products that a patron might find irresistible. (Photo courtesy of The Smithsonian Institution.)

hat on because the Tsar's picture was prominently displayed above the prescription department.

My wages were five dollars a week for a seven day week (about 65 hours). My duties outside of those of an apprentice included baby sitting, taking care of the heating system and some other chores for his wife. I worked hard and received periodic raises. . . .

In a couple of years I was promoted to a full-fledged junior clerk. My salary was now $12.00 a week. I engaged a private tutor [and] in 1908 I passed the regents examinations. . . . I entered Columbia College of Pharmacy in 1909, continuing to work at the same job.

I purchased my first drug store in 1912 in the Brownsville section of Brooklyn with the financial aid of my younger brother. . . . The store took in about $17.00 a day, mostly in prescriptions. . . . I had no help, except for the valuable aid of my wife, but I was young and ambitious. I even installed a night bell and answered quite a few night calls [when] we lived above the store. One morning about 3 o'clock, the bell rang. To make sure of waking me, an elderly lady pounded at the apartment door and said, "I have two prescriptions, please come down." Well, two prescriptions amounted to 70 cents—who could resist? Half awake I opened the store, put on the lights and was ready to go to work. But to my disappointment I learned that the "prescriptions" were just bait, because the lady said, "You should excuse me, I have no prescriptions. My daughter is going to have a baby, so I want 10 cents worth of licorice." Then she added, "No, no, make it 15 cents worth, after all I woke you up." . . .

The war [World War I] created chaotic conditions in the drug business. The supply of drugs and chemicals was inadequate, some were even unobtainable. Prices skyrocketed. . . . [The] situation was unbearable at times, but in spite of all difficulties the pharmacist did his utmost to fulfill his obligations and duties to the community. . . . The influenza epidemic of 1918 added extra burdens to the life of the pharmacist. He worked day and night to meet the demands of his profession. . . .

I sold my Brooklyn store . . . in 1919 and bought my second store in the same year on upper Park Avenue where the pushcart business was flourishing. It was a good prescription business. We employed two registered pharmacists and one junior. Things began to look up, life was more pleasant. I cut my working hours and spent more time with my family. . . . The pharmacist in a poor neighborhood has to be doctor, lawyer, priest and information bureau. People came in with all kinds of ridiculous inquiries. A man once asked me when the train leaves for Philadelphia. When I couldn't tell him, he did not think much of me as a pharmacist. He said, "Eh, you call yourself a druggist!"

I bought my last store in 1924, where I spent 36 years until I retired in 1960 at the age of 75. . . . Although some of these years were very harrowing, the pharmacist had become an important member of the public health team. . . . Someone asked me whether, if I had to do it over again, would I become a pharmacist. My answer is an emphatic "Yes." I am very proud of my profession in which I associated with wonderful and interesting people.

Richard Armour (b. 1906-d. 1989), Pomona, California, 1912-c. 1925

When my father took over the drug store, he inherited Harley. Harley was a large man with a happy round face and fair skin and curly red hair who spoke gently and walked on tiptoes as if he were afraid of waking someone. If there ever was an Indispensable Man, it was Harley. He knew where to find anything, from styptic pencils to rubber crutch tips and from ear stopples to spare parts for throat at-

The workaday environment of thousands of pharmacists in the 1920s was similar to that afforded by the Calkins Pharmacy in Columbus, Ohio. In size, stock, and decor, it was the American drugstore in transition. Packaged products are still shelved in wall cabinets under glass, although some sundries are open to self-service from a single island display. Up front are small tobacco and candy sections; in the back is a small soda fountain, which screens the prescription department from view. (From the Drug Topics Collection, AIHP.)

omizers. He also knew the wholesale price, the retail price, the name and address of every regular customer, and how to fill a small-necked bottle without spilling a drop. Most important, Harley knew how to make my father think my father was running the store, when the only running my father did was to Harley to find out something. . . .

My first assignment . . . as soon as I was able to count to twenty, was the responsible task of filling small white cardboard boxes with Armour's Cold Tablets. . . . It never occurred to me that Armour's Cold Tablets might not cure colds, because didn't everyone who took them eventually dry up? Besides, they were such large, bright red tablets that they made you feel better just to look at them. . . . [They] were as cheerful as holly berries and big enough to make an impression as they went down. The cold tablets were my grandfather's formula, but they were manufactured for us by Parke, Davis and Company. . . .

The part of the drug store I loved most, and not only because my grandmother was excluded from it, was the prescription room. Here a druggist, instead of being a merchant, was a chemist, a man of science. Our prescription room was like a laboratory. It was also like the bridge of a ship, for here my father, Harley and I, like the captain and first mate and cabin boy, seemed to be navigating perilous seas, now and then peering through a tiny porthole to see what was going on forward. . . .

To me, the prescription room was a mysterious, fascinating place, where druggists miraculously deciphered doctors' handwriting, mixed compounds with mortar, pestle and spatula, and poured disease-curing potions from one graduated beaker into another. Beakers, mortars, pestles, and spatulas eventually wound up in the sink to the rear of the prescription room, and I had the privilege of scouring away exotic smells and stains, some of which clung persistently, despite my best efforts. . . .

There was one job for which I was qualified and in which I delighted. This was making suppositories. Of course Harley or my father mixed the ingredients, the base of which was cocoa butter, but the actual turning out of the suppositories like so many cream-colored bullets, was delegated to me. Seldom have I had such a feeling of achievement and creativity. . . . The material itself having been turned over to me, I placed it in a machine of black-painted cast iron which was bolted securely to the wooden counter at which the druggist worked. Then I turned a handle, as though closing a vise, until the material was forced into bullet-shaped holes that looked like the chambers of a six-shooter. . . . When I had finished . . . all I had was suppositories, about .30 caliber ones.

This might seem easy . . . and easy it was except in summer, when the temperature rises to well over 100 degrees. . . . Then, unless cracked ice was applied to it, the cocoa butter, which melted at body

This cold-compression suppository machine, patented in 1895, eventually replaced other models and reduced the time and trouble attendant upon earlier hand methods. By rotating a wheel (as shown), the pharmacist created pressure in a cylinder filled with a previously prepared suppository mass. At the opposite end of the cylinder an interchange-able mould assured suppositories of proper size and shape, whether rectal, vaginal, or urethral.

heat, became too soggy to force into the mold. So I had to hold cracked ice to the top of the machine with one hand while turning the handle with the other. . . .

For several years, quite wisely, I was not permitted to wait on customers. Had we had a soda fountain, I would early have become a soda jerker, or a soda jerker's assistant, which is surely the best part of being a druggist's son. But my father, like my grandfather, was an old-time druggist, and to him a soda fountain had no more place in a drug store than a pool table in a bank. . . .

In time, however, I was considered mature enough to wait on la-dies at the perfume counter during the rush hour. . . . The perfume counter was the first one on the right when you entered the store, directly opposite the cigar counter. Men and women were thus separated before they had taken two steps into the store. If they came together again, it was at the counter in the rear where we displayed cold cures, which were of equal concern to both sexes. . . .

The way to sell perfume was to pull out stopper after stopper and wave it gently in front of the customer, who leaned over the counter within sniffing range. Once the customer had decided on the scent and the quantity, the perfume was poured into a graduated beaker and then into a small bottle or vial. This was taken back to the prescription room, where the name of the perfume would be typed on a label which was pasted onto the bottle. . . .

There were problems about selling perfume, as there seemed to be around everything around the drug store. For one thing it was necessary to restrain a customer, without being thought niggardly, from sniffing too many odors. Overexposure meant loss through evaporation for the proprietor and olfactory confusion for the customer. It was disheartening when some lady, nostrils all atwitch, would say she was unable to tell which was which and would have to come back some other day and make a fresh start. . . .

Another hazard of perfume selling was pouring into a small vial without having all the profits run down the sides. . . . After each sale . . . the beaker had to be taken back to the sink and carefully scrubbed with a wire brush and soap. . . . Since I spent much of my time at the sink, alternately washing out perfume beakers and scouring the utensils used in filling prescriptions, I usually went home laden with the delicate odors of lilac, lily of the valley, and ammonia, against a somewhat heavier background of iodoform and carbolic acid. . . . A sad-eyed, puny lad in knickers, with long twisted black stockings that matched my long, twisted black hair, I was now a druggist, junior grade. If I did not have the look of a pharmacist, at least I had the smell.

(Copyright 1959, by McGraw-Hill Book Company)

George A. Seyfarth (b. 1904), Chicago, Illinois, c. 1918-1930

We're talking about the "teens" and "twenties," when we sold leeches to take the "bad blood" out of black eyes (fifty cents). If you wanted them to get off the skin, just sprinkle a bit of salt on their tails. Citrate of Magnesia was made from scratch: Magnesium Carbonate, Citric Acid, Distilled Water, a little Lemon Oil, some Syrup—and let'er fizz. Dispense in a specially stoppered 12-ounce bottle, drop in a 32-grain Sodium Bicarb tablet and fasten the stopper. Provided you took the content of the whole bottle, you could almost guarantee action in a half hour.

Would you believe Diacetyl Morphine (Heroin) was present in some cough medicine? . . . Paregoric could be sold over the counter without [the customer] signing for it, to sooth baby's teething gums and for diarrhea. Vanilla Extract (Tincture Vanilla, N.F.), made with

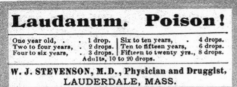

No. 6301. 1000, 60 cts. 500, 40 cts. 250, 30 cts.

Laudanum. Poison!

One year old,	1 drop.	Six to ten years,	4 drops.
Two to four years,	2 drops.	Ten to fifteen years,	6 drops.
Four to six years,	3 drops.	Fifteen to twenty yrs.,	8 drops.
	Adults, 10 to 20 drops.		

W. J. STEVENSON, M.D., Physician and Druggist,
LAUDERDALE, MASS.

No. 6302. 1000, 60 cts. 500, 40 cts. 250, 30 cts.

Tincture of Arnica.

For Sprains, Bruises and Lameness of any kind. Used externally.

W. A. ALEXANDER, Druggist,
West side Main Street, opposite Court House, LEON, IOWA.

No. 6303. 1000, 60 cts. 500, 40 cts. 250, 30 cts.

Seidlitz Powders.

Dissolve the contents of a blue and a white paper separately in one-fourth of a tumbler of water. Then pour one solution into the other and drink immediately.

MANSFIELD'S DRUG STORE,
516 Main Street,   -   SPRINGFIELD, MASS.

No. 6304. 1000, 60 cts. 500, 40 cts. 250, 30 cts.

Spirits of Camphor.

DOSE.—From five drops to a teaspoonful, first added to sugar and then mixed with water.

J. REHM, Druggist,
West 75th Street,   GRAND CROSSING, ILL.

Nineteenth-century pharmacists recalled long hours devoted to replenishing their stock of home remedies called "druggists preparations." These were manufactured in the pharmacy or were, increasingly, purchased in bulk from a large-scale manufacturing laboratory, then packaged under the pharmacist's own label. A few examples of customized labels available in 1893 are reproduced here from the catalog of the Merchants Publishing Co., Chicago.

real vanilla beans, was largely sold in drug stores. We sold whole vanilla beans for five cents each. . . . The drug store was the source of
most spices in those days.

Yes, we were actually "pill rollers," combining honey, licorice
powder, plus the [active] drug, and rolling them into pills. Then we
powdered them with lycopodium to make them neat [and not stick
together]. . . . An attractive green, Eskay's Neurophosphates made
with wine was a prime favorite with the medics for a good nerve tonic.
. . . For bedridden flu patients, the rule was to light a Vapo-Cresoline
Lamp by the bedside, and the cresol vapors chased the flu bug right
out—while the fumes spread to stink up the whole house. . . . Recti-
fied Oil of Turpentine was used drop-wise on sugar for kidney infec-
tions. . . . [Foul-smelling] Asafoetida Gum was in demand—and still
is in some neighborhoods [1970s]—to ward off colds and other diseases when hung around the neck. . . . Bitter tonics had 20% to 25%
Alcohol and were widely used as tonics [even] by those who bitterly
condemned alcohol [use]. . . .

[While] at Sargent's Drug Store in Chicago (500 scrips a day!)
we made Cold Cream (Unguentum Aquae Rosae)—spermaceti, white
wax, sweet almond oil, borax, and rose water—in 50-pound lots with
the aid of an ointment mill. . . . In those days we received prescriptions to put about six powdered [botanical] drugs into a vehicle of
Elixir Lactated Pepsin that positively would not dissolve completely.
All we could do was use a Shake label, and caution the patient so he
would get even doses of the drugs. . . . My father used to dispense prescription bottles with a colored paper cap tied on with a red string—
people were impressed.

[Popular] headache products were Orangeine Headache Powders, Anti-Kamnia Tablets, Pyramidon Tablets. [Popular medici-
nal] teas were Hamburger Breast Tea, Garfield Tea, and Schoenfeld
Tea. . . . Seidlitz Powders [sold well] for headache and stomach,
[the contents of] one blue and one white powder paper, each to be
dissolved in separate glasses, then poured together while fizzing—
never, no never, to be taken separately. . . .

[Federal "Prohibition" had become effective in 1920.] As a pharmacist I well recall the U.S. government triplicate prescription forms,
. . . from the Treasury Department, which was made responsible for
enforcement of Prohibition in 1930: . . . One copy was retained by

the physician, . . . one was given to the patient to have the prescription [for medicinal alcohol] filled by his pharmacist, and a third form was sent back to the government as a record. It was a lot of paperwork. . . . It turned out that more than a few [physicians] became greedy and produced additional revenue by virtually "selling" these prescriptions to very, very "ill" patients whose principal complaint was a ceaseless search for John Barleycorn and the tasty fluids of Bacchus. . . . I am sorry to say that many pharmacists entered the wild scramble for profits from illegal liquor, and ethics became a system of behavior for the other fellow.

Legal alcohol supplied to hospitals, pharmacies and dental offices often was diverted into other than medical channels. [For example,] I

The physiologic effects of alcohol, long valued in medicine, gained added respectability in therapeutics after about 1860. But with the advent of "Prohibition," medicinal alcohol could be dispensed legally only when prescribed on a triplicate form issued by the Federal government. Several reminiscences hint at a scandalous increase of illnesses requiring "medicinal" alcohol during these years (e.g., Pharmacist Seyfarth's testimony, above).

High-jinks after hours in an East-coast drugstore sometime in the late 1800s. Each clerk, dressed for the occasion, holds toward the camera something emblematic of his life behind the counter—including an early-model telephone (lower left). Pharmacist George Seyfarth recalls (below) that during Prohibition such partying was occasionally lubricated with medicinal alcohol from the prescription-room. (Photo courtesy of 1199 Drug News, December 1958, *and Isaac Dallin.)*

remember lights in dental offices late into the night and sessions behind the prescription counter of pharmacies, long after they had closed the doors, where "happy hours" were frequent. . . . Such was the turmoil of Prohibition during the wild twenties and thirties that the United States had had it by 1933, and on December 5th the Eighteenth Amendment to the Constitution was repealed.

. . . In my early years in drug stores people expected a distinctive smell, often from the spices and [medicinal] herbs and sometimes from the chemicals we used in compounding prescriptions. Sometimes the latter would get quite malodorous when mixed. The spices have gone to the supermarkets, the herbs are sold in "health stores," and we don't compound much anymore; so there isn't much odor left, [all gone:] the smells, perfumes, scents, aromas, effluvia, fragrances—musty, acrid, foul, savory, or pungent.

Jacob Eisen (b. 1901-d. 1993), Newark, New Jersey, 1920-1950

Testimony in court proceedings, 1952, on direct examination by counsel for the Board of Pharmacy of the State of New Jersey:

Q. Are you a pharmacist in the State of New Jersey. A. Yes, sir. . . .

Q. Are you presently engaged in the operation of a retail pharmacy? A. Yes, sir. . . .

Q. Do you take precautions in the sale of packaged drugs and medicines to consumers? A. Yes, sir.

Q. Will you describe the nature of the precautions? A. It depends a great deal upon who the customer is who is making the purchase. If we think that an over-dose might be the thing involved, we caution them very carefully about reading the label and precautions on the package, and warning them not to take any more than the individual label shows.

Though medicines and other health supplies gave drugstores their essential character, survival usually depended on sidelines, such as the soda fountain— which proved irresistible to passersby. A fountain typical of the 1920s is featured in this view of part of Clock's pharmacy in Brighton, Colorado. The male staff seems upstaged by the full-size cutout of a woman eager to take Zymole Trokeys for her "husky throat." (Photo copyright by Denver Public Library.)

Q. Have you had occasion in your store to serve a person who could not read? A. Very often.

Q. Do you take any extra precautions with respect to them? A. Yes, sir. We read the label for them, giving them all the necessary instructions that they should receive, in as simple English as we can.

Q. In the sale of packaged drugs and medicines, as between one drug and another, for example, Laxol and Lysol, do you take any special precautions? A. Yes. That happens frequently, that the names are mispronounced. There are many names on packaged goods that are very similar, as you just mentioned.

Q. Can you give me a few examples of the similarity in the names of packaged drugs and medicines. A. Yes, sir. Borax and Boric Acid are confused often. Laxol and Lysol, which you mentioned. . . .

Q. Any others like that: Yes Argyrol and Agarol. . . . Eyegene and iodine. . . .

Q. Do you take any special precautions when the customer is old, debilitated or enfeebled. A. Yes, sir.

Q. What is the nature of the precaution in that case? A. First we make sure we know what they want. Then we make up our minds whether there is anything in that particular package that might be harmful to an elderly person. We warn them about it. Perhaps in some case we may even refuse to sell.

Q. I show you Exhibit D-34 . . . and ask you whether with respect to that product, Miles' One-A-Day Vitamins, any special care in the handling in your store of that product takes place. A. Yes. In regard to the handling, it states that it should be kept in a cool dry place; do not expose it to direct sunlight or artificial heat.

Q. Where do you keep products of that kind in your store. A. In a cool place. Those requiring a little more than a cool place we keep in refrigerators. . . .

Q. Do you take any special precautions in your store with respect to sales to children? A. Yes, sir, we try to avoid selling to children under thirteen or twelve anything we think might be dangerous.

Q. Now in the practice of pharmacy . . . have you had occasion to take what might be termed refresher courses from time to time? A. Oh, definitely. I have taken refresher courses at Rutgers University, College of Pharmacy for many years since the war and prior to the war every year.

Q. Now in the practice of being a druggist or pharmacist do you have available texts or authorities that you rely on in the practice of your profession? A. Yes, sir.

Q. Can you name a few of them? A. Yes, sir, United States Pharmacopoeia; all the copies that have been issued since I have become a pharmacist, and the same with the National Formulary and the Dispensatory, Remington's Practice of Pharmacy, Husa's Practice of Pharmacy, the NNR—that is the New and Non-official Remedies— various magazines and periodicals, scientific periodicals. . . .

Q. Have you ever communicated with a doctor about the over-the-counter packaged drug other than a prescription item. A. Yes, sir, I have. . . . Particularly one case I remember. . . . I knew this particular patient was a diabetic. She asked for something I knew she should not take. She assured me that that is what her physician told her to take, but I verified it.

Q. By verifying it you mean you called the physician? A. Yes, I called the physician.

Q. What did the physician tell you? A. That she obviously misunderstood him.

Q. And the sale was not made? A. The sale was not made. . . .

On cross-examination by counsel for the Proprietary Association:

Q. Doctor, when you talked to these customers that come in to buy some of these packaged medicines, which you recognize as the proprietary, do you attempt to diagnose the condition of the customer? A. In what sense do you mean? You called me a doctor. I am not a physician.

Q. Then, Mr. Eisen. Do you attempt to diagnose the condition of the customer that comes to your counter to buy one of these packaged medicines? A. No, sir.

Q. Do you attempt to prescribe for him? A. Definitely not.

Q. Do you make any inquiries of him as to what his malady may be? A. If it is in reference to some medicine he is buying, where I can assist him, I may ask some general questions.

Q. We are talking about these so-called packaged or proprietary medicines. A. Definitely. On Vick's Vatronal I always ask questions or nearly always to find out if it is for an infant, to find out if it is for a very old person.

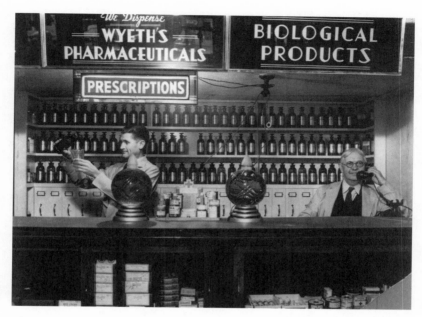

Pharmacists at work in 1936 at the Williams Avolawn Pharmacy, Dallas, Texas. This prescription department suggests a time of transition between old and new. Prescription work has been opened to public view. The pharmacy's "Biological Products" all had been introduced within the memory of the older pharmacist here on duty. Symbolic showglobes of old tradition grace the counter in the modern guise of art-deco design. Back of the counter, new Schwartz cabinets hold packaged proprietary drugs that soon would make the traditional sets of bottles for non-proprietary drugs an anachronism. (From AIHP/Drug Topics Collection.)

Q. Do you ask questions also when you sell laxatives? A. I may not ask a question but I will give some information.

Q. You will tell them whether it is a fast acting or slow acting laxative? A. No, sir. I will tell them not to take it if they have pains in the stomach because of the possibility of appendicitis.

Hubert H. Humphrey (b. 1911-d. 1978), Doland, Minnesota, c. 1927-1936

As a youth I spent long hours working and talking and listening to others in my father's drugstore. My lifelong understanding of farm

A chronic oversupply of drugstores in urban areas produced eventually an epidemic of "cut-rate" drugstores, such as Gordon-Abraham in Plattsburgh, New York. Those with a gift for aggressive merchandising prospered—especially the small, early chains in the late 19th century—but many others foundered in the intense competition. (From a postcard image in the William H. Helfand Collection.)

problems sprang from here, for my father also sold veterinary supplies and I made the rounds with him from farm to farm.

Our pharmacy sold far more to people than drugs and sodas. We traded in ideas as well, for my father was interested in everything from religion to politics and from symphonic music to poetry. When the dust storms hit the Great Plains in the late 1920s, our drugstore counter raged with discussions about economics and politics.

With the onset of the depression my father's pharmacy in Doland failed and we moved to Huron and started again. I wanted to continue in college but family finances were too low. So to help my father in business, I took a six-month cram course in 1933 at the Denver College of Pharmacy.

In 1936 I received an opportunity to continue my college studies at the University of Minnesota. In a sense this was the beginning of the end of my formal career as a pharmacist, but even today [c. 1972] I remain personally involved in our family-owned [drug] business. . . . [But] the small-town world of Doland and Huron fell behind me as I moved rapidly into the world of politics. Many times in the years ahead I confronted difficulties, failure, and defeat, including losing the Presidency in 1968 by a narrow one-tenth of one per cent of the vote cast. [However,] the insights into human nature which I gained as a young man had burned their way into my thoughts and life, and I knew I could never be other than optimistic about the future. . . .

(Copyright 1973, by Wm. L. Blockstein and C. Boyd Granberg)

Celia Frumer Handelman (b. 1906), Philadelphia, Pennsylvania, 1929-c. 1940

[I] studied pharmacy at the Des Moines College of Pharmacy after graduating from Drake, became an American citizen in 1927 . . . , completed the pharmacy course in a year, passed the Iowa State Board of Pharmacy examinations, and moved to Philadelphia.

For weeks I went from store to store fortified with my diploma, asking and pleading for a job, but apparently store owners had never

The way of "life behind the counter" recalled by contributors to Drugstore Memories *began to be influenced, after about 1900, by the development of chain drugstores such as this Chicago establishment (1949). Size expanded; sidelines multiplied; merchandising became aggressive; and the innovation of "self-service" changed the staffing pattern and traditional personality of the "corner drugstore," whether chain or independent. (Photo courtesy of Walgreen Drugstores and the AIHP Drug Topics Collection.)*

seen a woman pharmacist. . . . Finally, I decided to buy a store although I had no money. . . . I found a small drug store at the corner of
4th and Wolf Sts. in a growing Jewish neighborhood. . . . Living quarters were in the back and upstairs. The asking price was $5,750. I bor-
rowed the down payment of $300 from a bank, using my husband's
salary as collateral, and bought the store in 1930. . . .

At first I could not overcome the prejudice against a woman
pharmacist. Even though I had my diploma right up front, they
did not want to leave prescriptions with me. . . . To promote the
store, I opened accounts with [drug companies] . . . which stocked
the store. . . . We advertised that if you couldn't get what you
wanted elsewhere, we would have it or get it for you. . . . I visited
doctors in the area. . . . Soon prescriptions came from the doctors,
and I [even] needed more help. We made our own capsules, powders, ointments, cough medicines, headache medicines and even
suppositories, which was very time and space consuming.

We opened at 8 in the morning and closed at midnight. My hus-
band was able to help me only until 3 P.M. and then after 10 P.M.
These long hours paid off, and we had to enlarge the store. . . . Our
only son, Sholom, . . . seeing how hard we worked, decided never to
be a pharmacist. . . [But] pharmacy is an ideal and natural profession
for women even though it is so different from when I started.

William Byron Rumford, Sr. (b. 1908-d. 1986), Berkeley, California, 1930-1950.

. . . I was fortunate in finding a job parking cars at night while
attending school in the day [at the University of California College of
Pharmacy]. . . . I graduated from the College in June 1931, a depression year when jobs were very hard to come by. This was the big moment for me, as I recalled my beginning [as a stock boy] at the Sun
Drug Company in Phoenix, Arizona. . . .

My first licentiate employment was with a community pharmacy
at the prevailing low salary; nevertheless, the job provided valuable
and necessary experience. I liked my job and the people I met on the
job. My next opportunity in the practice of my profession was on the
pharmacy staff at the county hospital as a civil servant. This employment was completely different from community pharmacy. It afforded

me the chance to practice basic pharmacy, and I remained for more than eight years.

In 1943 I had the opportunity to purchase the community pharmacy in which I took my apprenticeship. By some careful financial manipulating of my meager savings, I was able to meet the agreement and to become a proprietor. . . .

During the next few years, I decided that I needed more academic training to accompany my almost completely scientific training and enrolled at the University of California at Berkeley. In 1948 I graduated in political science—accomplished while I worked my full eight hours in the store.

It was during this same year that my many friends in the community asked me to seek a seat in the State legislature. . . . It marked the beginning of a dual career. . . . I was re-elected for nine consecutive terms as Assemblyman from the 17th District. Fifteen of these years I served as chairman of the Assembly Committee on Public Health. My training in pharmacy kept me in the forefront on all public health matters and bills concerning the health professions. . . . [For example, Rumford wrote or sponsored state laws on fair housing, anti-pollution, anti-discrimination, and fair employment practices.—Eds.] Although immersed in duties in the State legislature, I was able to expand my pharmacy [in Berkeley] and construct a new building to house a modern establishment. . . . Pharmacy is deeply imbedded in my heart and in my life.

Carl E. Kyburz (b. 1915-d. 1987), Chatsworth, Illinois, 1933

Why would Mr. Quinn want to see me on a summer day in 1933, while I was working in a hay field of my father's farm, near Chatworth, Illinois? . . . It turned out that Mr. Quinn wanted me to work for him, and he helped prepare me for pharmacy school. Mr. Quinn was proud of his profession and wanted his employees to feel the same way. He was a fine teacher and he wanted the new boy first to learn the arts of shopkeeping: how to ring the register, to check out at night and open in the morning, to wrap a small package without using string, and to "wait on customers" properly. . . .

There wasn't much I missed in the way of experience during the next three years. We had a complete stock. . . . Large barrels of turpentine, linseed oil, and kerosene were purchased and put in the basement. . . . I got so I could pour out a gallon of castor oil into one-and two-ounce bottles without spilling a drop. We sold a variety of goods: for example, paints, perfumes, and garden seeds. Some items sold for only ten cents, such as tooth paste, corn remover, colognes, talcum, soap, shaving cream, and hair oils. . . . As an apprentice my duties were varied, including trimming wallpaper for customers—a service then traditional among many small-town drugstores. . . .

Corner drugstores had been a gathering place of neighborhoods for decades, but ours was exceptional because our street was a dead-end and also was a stop for the trolley line! So going or coming, everyone ended their trip in front of the drugstore or came in to say hello. As the months passed, it seemed ordained that I was to be a pharmacist and off I went to the Indianapolis College of Pharmacy.

Bibliography

Note: Only the documents excerpted in the main text are cited below. A document indicated as "In KRF" means the complete source can be found in the Kremers Reference Files, School of Pharmacy, University of Wisconsin-Madison. Entries are arranged alphabetically by surnames of the contributing pharmacists.

Alpers, William C., letters to Edward Kremers, Madison, WI, 1 January 1898 and 20 November 1899, in KRF ("A2:Alpers").

Armour, Richard. *Drug Store Days: My Youth Among the Pills and Potions.* New York: McGraw-Hill Book Company, 1959. 48-52, 177.

Ballard, John W., in: Anon., "Old-Time Iowa Druggists," *Druggists Circular* 51(1907):193.

Balloff, George H., "Five Decades a Pharmacist," typescript at Bentley Historical Library, University of Michigan, Ann Arbor, MI.

Baxley, J. Brown, in: M. R. Culbreth, "Reminiscences of Early Pharmacy in Baltimore," *Journal of the American Pharmaceutical Association* 19(1930):286-288.

Beal, James Hartley, "Partial Confession of James Hartley Beal," typescript in KRF ("A2:Beal.").

Best, John, "Reminiscences of Pharmacy in the Rockies," *Journal of the American Pharmaceutical Association* 2(1913):325-327.

Brewer, William A., Sr., "Reminiscences of an Old Pharmacist," *Pharmaceutical Record* 4(1884): 210 f., 232 f., 255 f., 282 f., 304 f., 326 f., 348, 410 f., 424 f., 442 f., 460 f., 475, 494; and 5(1885): 6, 23, 38, 54, 71 f., 89 f., 122 f., 138, 169.

Carstarphen, W. P., in: A. C. Meyer. *The Earlier Years of the Drug and Allied Trades in the Mississippi Valley.* Saint Louis: privately printed, 1948. 150-152.

Cook, Roy Bird, in: *The Remington [Medal] Lectures.* Edited by G. B. Griffenhagen, W. L. Blockstein, and D. J. Krigstein. Washington DC: American Pharmaceutical Association, 1994. 187 f.

Cousins, Walter Henry, to Edward Kremers, 2 December 1932. 4-p. ms. and "Autobiography of Walter Henry Cousins," 1925, 4-p. ms., both in KRF ("A2:Cousins"); also "Chuck Wagon Therapy . . . ," *Journal of the American Pharmaceutical Association* 25(1936):877-882. We have combined passages from the three sources into a single excerpt.

Dadd, John A., "Paper Read by John A. Dadd of Milwaukee to the Graduating Class, Dept. of Pharmacy, June 1894, University of Wisconsin," *Proceedings of the Wisconsin Pharmaceutical Association* . . . 1894: 97-101.

Dimmitt, Fred R., "The Drug Business in Missouri in Earlier Days," *Druggists Circular* 51(1907):189.

DuBois, W. L., "My Early Impressions of the Drug Business [in New York]," *Journal of the American Pharmaceutical Association* 6(1917): 273-276.

Eisen, Jacob. Testimony in Superior Court of New Jersey, Appellate Division, Docket No. A-74-53, The Proprietary Association vs. Board of Pharmacy of the State of New Jersey, Joint Appendix of Vol. II. Newark NJ, 1952, 412a-415a.

Ellis, E. T., "Story of a Very Old Philadelphia Drugstore," *American Journal of Pharmacy* 75(1903): 57 ff.

Emich, C. V., "The Pharmacy of Fifty Years Ago," *Proceedings of the American Pharmaceutical Association* 50(1902):539-542.

Fenn, Frederick W., "Delaware Druggist of the Older Days," *Druggists Circular* 51(1907):181.

Flexner, Jacob A., "A Vanishing Profession," *Atlantic Monthly* 148(1931), No. 1:16-25.

Forbes, James Winchell, "The Memoirs of an American Pharmacist." Edited by J. H. Beal, *Midland Druggist and Pharmaceutical Review,* 45(1911): (III)388, (IV)442, (V)487, (VI)536. 46(1912): (VII)18, (VIII)58, (IX)104, (X)150, (XI)194, (XII)238, (XIII)282, (XIV)327, (XV)376, (XVI)411. Parts of Forbes' manuscript that were published by editor Beal, but not excerpted here (largely non-pharmacy), can be found at: *ibid.* 45(1911): (I)289, (II)337, (IV)442. 46(1912): (XVII)467, (XVIII)512. 47(1913): (XIX)13, (XX)69,

(XXI)114, (XXII)172. See also, J. H. Beal, "How the Forbes Memoirs Came To Be Written," *ibid.* 47(1913): 160 f.

Gordon, F. T., "The Naval Apothecary Since the Civil War—Some Historical Data and Personal Reminiscences," *Journal of the American Pharmaceutical Association* 2(1913):57-63.

Gray, John W., letter to Louis K. Liggett, in: Louis K. Liggett, "Pharmacy in the Past Twenty-five Years," *Pharmaceutical Era* 47(1914):52.

Hancock, John F., "Reminiscences Pharmaceutical," *Druggists Circular* 51(1907):181 f.

Handelman, Celia Frumer, in *Compounding WAS More Fun!!—Life Experiences of Women of Lambda Kappa Sigma. . . . ,* Frances F. Curran, ed., n.p., c. 1988. 39-41.

Harris, Ernest L., "A Page from the Past: Pharmacy in St. Louis, Missouri," *Journal of the National Pharmaceutical Association* 1, No. 1(1954):9 & 21.

Howard, Carrie E., "An Inaugural Essay on Women as Pharmacists," ms. in Joseph W. England Library, Philadelphia College of Pharmacy, University of the Sciences in Philadelphia, 1890. 12 pp. Kindly called to our attention by Mignon S. Adams, Chair, Libraries and Educational Resources, and Michael A. Ermilio, Archivist.

Huger, B. C., in: A. C. Meyer. *The Earlier Years of the Drug and Allied Trades in the Mississippi Valley,* Saint Louis: privately printed, 1948. 146-149.

Humphrey, Hubert H., in: *Remarkable Pharmacists.* Edited by Wm. L. Blockstein and C. Boyd Granberg. West Des Moines IA: RobLee Hill, 1973. 148 f.

Hurty, J. N., "Drug Store Recollections," *Journal of the American Pharmaceutical Association* 7(1918):625-629.

Johnson, Charles B., *Muskets and Medicine, or Army Life in the Sixties.* Philadelphia: F. A. Davis Co., 1917. 58, 112, 127-130. Brought to our attention by Michael A. Flannery.

Kilmer, Fred B., "Drug Clerks One Hundred Years Ago," *Journal of the American Pharmaceutical Association* 18(1929):711-722.

Kremers, Edward, "Dem Andenken an Louis Lotz," *Badger Pharmacist,* No. 8(1936):Feb., 7-10. Excerpt translated for this anthology.

Kyburz, Carl E., "Beginnings of a Pharmacist: A Reminiscence," *Pharmacy in History* 25(1983):30-32.

Lemberger, Joseph L., "The Drug Apprentice of the Early Days of the American Pharmaceutical Association," *Proceedings of the American Pharmaceutical Association* 55(1907):575 f.

Lloyd, John Uri, "A Pharmaceutical Apprenticeship in America Fifty Years Ago," *Journal of the American Pharmaceutical Association* 4(1915):1333.

Magoffin, Albert E., "Recollections of an Old-Time Druggist," *Druggists Circular* 51(1907):192 f.

Maisch, John, as: Translation of Father's Autobiographical Notes, 8 August 1879, among Maisch Documents, Joseph W. England Library, The University of the Sciences in Philadelphia.

Meyer, A. C. *The Earlier Years of the Drug and Allied Trades in the Mississippi Valley*. St. Louis: privately printed, 1948. 22-24 and 157-159.

Meyer, Christian Frederick G., in: A. C. Meyer, *ibid.*, 8 f.

Moore, J. T., "The Early Days of Pharmacy in the West," *Journal of the American Pharmaceutical Association* 25(1936):705-715.

Muth, M. Joseph, as quoted in: M. R. Culbreth, "Reminiscences of Early Pharmacy in Baltimore," *ibid.* 19(1930):282-284.

Noll, Mathias, "Past and Present Observations of Drug Stores," *ibid.* 27(1938):812 f.

Pancoast, Charles E. *A Quaker Forty-Niner; The Adventures of Charles Edward Pancoast on the American Frontier*. Edited by Anna Paschall Hannum. Philadelphia: University of Pennsylvania Press, 1930. 14-19, 23, 25, 39-40, 93-94.

Parchen, H. M., "Early Days of Montana Pharmacy," *Druggists Circular* 51(1907):191.

Parrish, Edward, "Pharmacy As a Business," *Proceedings of the American Pharmaceutical Association* 5(1856):59-68.

Philips, Shine. *Big Spring; The Casual Biography of a Prairie Town*. New York: Prentice-Hall, Inc., 1942. 23, 25 f., 28, 31, 33 f., 37, 49 f., 52, 111 f.

Rogers, William H., "Looking Backward Over New York State," *Druggists Circular* 51(1907):169 f.

Rumford, William B., in: *Remarkable Pharmacists*. Edited by Wm. L. Blockstein & C. Boyd Granberg. West Des Moines, Iowa: RobLee Hill, 1973. 122 f.

Seyfarth, George A., Reminiscence, ms. 13 pp., with letter of transmittal 27 May 1985, in KRF ("C44(a)").

Sharp, Alpheus., as quoted in: David M. R. Culbreth, "Reminiscences of Early Pharmacy in Baltimore," *Journal of the American Pharmaceutical Association* 19(1930):285 f.

Sheppard, S. A. D., "Some Old New England Druggists," *Druggists Circular* 51(1907):Jan., 171.

Shoemaker, Robert, "The Apothecary's Apprentice," *American Journal of Pharmacy* 52(1880):65-69.

Simms, G. G. C., "Washington City a Half-Century Ago," *Druggists Circular* 51(1907): No. 1, 183.

Stuart, Josephine W., in *Pharmaceutical Era*, 45(1912):104, 181. A letter to Emma Gary Wallace, for her series on women in pharmacy.

Thurber, George. A druggist's diary of 1841-42 as transcribed by Edward Kremers c. 1931-32, ms. KRF ("A2:Thurber").

Wardell, Theodore R., "An Old New Yorker in Georgia," *Druggists Circular* 51(1907): No. 1, 168.

Wenzell, William T. to Edward Kremers, 7 September 1903, a holograph memoir, 5 pp;. and 20 October 1903, continuation of memoir, 5 pp. In: KRF ("A2:Wenzell"). Our excerpt combines inter-related passages from both documents.

Zahn, Charles H., in: A. C. Meyer. *The Earlier Years of the Drug and Allied Trades in the Mississippi Valley*. Saint Louis: privately printed, 1948. 105 f.

Zielin, J. H., "Drug Business in the Late Confederate States," *Western Druggist* 11(1889):448 f.

Author Index